the girl with the   , hair

What I have learned about Life

Alis Rowe

Published by
Lonely Mind Books
London

"Alis Rowe writes complex psychological material with such simplicity and dead on truth."

the girl with the curly hair

What I have learned about Life

Alis Rowe

Preface

Today I decide to write the follow on to 'Asperger's and Me'. The motivation for writing this second book came from an email that I received yesterday. The email said:

"Asperger's and Me is the most amazing book I've ever read. I would love to read another book similar or just another book of yours. Your writing style is just so amazing and incredible."

And I replied:
"I'll be writing part 2 in the future!!"

The future happened to be the following day.

The first thing I did as I started writing was to change the font and the size. I think this is a good example of one of my ASD traits. I can't ever type anything unless I've changed the font first. The right font just makes my writing look 'right'. It's a little strategy I've learned to help me get started.

Everyone who is reading this will no doubt already know quite a lot about me just from having read 'Asperger's and Me', and maybe by reading my blog and social media posts. I do feel however, that I keep my day to day life quite private. I've been described as being remote and mysterious and that I keep a lot of things to myself.

I've been thinking about writing a second [long] book for a couple of years. A lot of people have been asking me to.

But there were some barriers, the main one – and obviously this was a big one – was that I hadn't got enough content about my life for another book!! At least with the first one, there was lots of content, as I had over 20 years of 'life' to cover. Now writing this one I've only had about 5 years of life to cover and, in that time, my life hasn't really changed. I've had far less 'big' experiences in the last 5 years than before. This is an interesting thing to note in itself – as a child and young adult I was exposed to many different things (most not my own choice) such as: education, holidays, socialising, going out and extracurricular activities. Now, as an adult, I don't really do any of these things (out of choice). All that participation in things I didn't want to do was very, very stressful, but the positives are that doing them has given me a much broader perspective and understanding of others, myself, and the world at large.

So, what exactly do I do now and if I don't do much at all how can I write a long book about my life? Now you can see the dilemma I was facing!

This book therefore, is less about what I do and have done, and more about *how I think and how I see the world* since understanding my condition. This book gives lots of insight into how I think but also has a big focus on the strategies I use that help me cope.

Alis

xxx

Acronyms used:
ASD (Autism Spectrum Disorder)
CHP (Curly Hair Project)
NT (Neurotypical, meaning a person without ASD)

How I refer to ASD:
I use a variety of language to talk about ASD/autism/Asperger's Syndrome (they all mean the same thing). I use language interchangeably so you will see a variety of phrases and words in this book and I intend them to mean the same thing:
"Person with autism/ASD"
"Autistic person"
"Has autism/ASD"
"Person on the [autistic] spectrum"

Contents

WHAT i HAVE LEARNED ABOUT CHANGE

Small changes
Big changes
Changing people

Changes make me very, very anxious. You can be assured that if a change has taken place in my life, it probably will not have been me who initiated it. If it was me, believe me it was not done without an enormous amount of stress.

There are lots of different types of change and all are anxiety-provoking:

- Small changes, such as a change in plan of the day
- Big changes, such as the different periods in one's life, or specific events
- People who have changed

My dislike of change is largely to do with how my life is carefully arranged. Because I think situations through in so much detail and because I am so rigid and meticulous about what I do each day, any change in any one aspect of my life is going to affect everything else. It is so disruptive. Change is therefore probably far more stressful for me than for someone who is more flexible and is happy to go-with-the-flow.

Small changes

Change can be small, such as a change to my plan for the day, or if I wake up and go across the road to collect my newspaper round to find that the newspapers have not yet arrived at the shop.

Small changes tend to ruin an entire day. Not only do I have difficulty rearranging my routine to accommodate for these changes, but I also have a problem calming down from the anxiety the change causes me to feel.

A small change in the day can also affect my emotions for the day. Whenever I plan to do something, I plan to feel the emotion that is associated with that particular task. I can predict that I am going to feel X and that X will linger for the rest of the day. But when that task gets changed, no longer do I get to feel X, I feel Y instead, and Y feels horrible and unexpected.

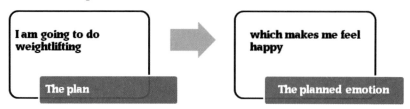

I am going to do weightlifting → **which makes me feel happy**

The plan   The planned emotion

Big changes

Big changes are to do with different stages in a person's life, such as leaving university or starting a new job. Big changes can also be caused by specific events such as the loss of a loved one, or a change in living circumstances.

Big changes can be really frightening.

An issue with big changes is that I find it really, really difficult to transition from how-something-is-now to how-something-becomes. Because of this, it is incredibly difficult for me to 'move on' at the same rate as life is moving on. Big changes cause me become 'stuck'.

Some big changes cause me to go through an intense, grieving process in which I yearn for life to go back to how it was before.

Some of the big changes that have happened to me in the last few years include: leaving university, the loss of family members and pets, my sister leaving home, my parents no longer being together, getting a dog, my other half moving house, no longer seeing my friends, getting injured, leaving a job, starting a new job and making changes to my business.

Some of these changes are actually quite positive: I have left jobs that I disliked, I have improved how my business runs, my sister left home and is now happily living with her boyfriend… but even positive changes can mean that I grieve. To be honest, one of the only few changes that I have felt solely positive about and did not grieve for was leaving school and that was because I was unhappy with what felt like 95% of my life during that period (because I was so depressed). When I left school, I started to enjoy other aspects of life again. Most other changes always cause me to grieve.

Grieving is not necessarily over the specific aspect that has changed. It usually happens over the aspects of life that are associated with the change. For example, I felt positive to leave a job that I disliked, but I felt unhappy because I would miss the routine it had given me, the walk to and from that place of work, and I would miss the people I liked who worked there.

Changes also have a negative effect on me because I crave stability and predictability and to have control of my life. For example, even during the time I was working in a job that I strongly disliked, at least my life was stable. Life was predictable and I had a routine that included my job.

A problem that arises after something changes is a period of time in which lots of things feel "different" and "new", causing life to feel "unstable". This is what I call the 'transition period' and this for me is very anxiety-provoking:

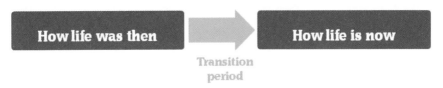

For example, after my sister moved out of home, life felt very, very unstable. It was even very strange doing my weightlifting in the morning knowing that she wouldn't be complaining about the noise! I was used to experiencing this as part of my daily routine because when I did weightlifting in the morning, my sister would get cross and tells me to stop because it was waking her up.

It's a bit like a logical equation. IF [this] happens, THEN [that] happens. How unnerving it feels when the THEN part does not happen.

When my mum retired, it was very odd that she was no longer coming home regularly at 5.45pm. I was used to experiencing life as: when at 5.45pm the front door opens, Mum gets home.

Other people's changes affect my experience of life and I find that really hard. I have my own world and other people have their own world, but there is also a shared world.

I always try to keep my own world the same but someone else still has the potential to change my world because of that overlapping part in the middle.

Another example of how other people's changes affect my feelings of stability is that there used to always be a customer in the shop getting his newspaper every day when I went to collect my newspaper round. He was in his world and also overlapping into my world. A few days went by when I did not see him so I asked the owner of the shop where he was. The shop owner said that this customer could no longer walk properly so did not come anymore. I had no relationship with this customer other than seeing him regularly, but I was very sad to hear of his problem and I missed his presence. The world just felt a bit more unstable for a period of time until finally I adjusted to not seeing him.

Unfortunately, my rigidity in terms of trying to always keep things the same can cause an enormous amount of stress in other people who might not be able to or might not want to keep things the same. I don't mind when people make changes that affect just their world leaving mine unchanged, but I do mind when their changes affect my world because they are inside the overlapping part. I have noticed that I often drive for things to be kept the same even when the circumstances suggest that it is no longer convenient, practical or realistic. For example, why should my Mum have to continue opening the front door and coming into the house at 5.45pm every day, just so that my world was kept the same?

I remember when I was younger my grandparents used to collect me from school and as I got older they used to collect me from college. Then at some point my parents decided that it was time for me to be a bit more independent and that my grandparents did not need to collect me anymore. This was really hard to adjust to. I became very upset, and I grieved. In comparison, my neurotypical sister did not really care whether or not my grandparents were around! In fact, she was probably enjoying the freedom that this change had given her!

When a close friend of mine once lived near me we used to go walking together most days early in the mornings. After he moved house, I still wanted him to come and meet me to go walking exactly how we had always done previously. He got frustrated with me because I could not seem to accept that it was no longer easy for him to do this and that from now on we had to do things differently, e.g. to walk later in the day, walk only at weekends or I would have to go to the town where he lived and we could go walking there instead. I found this situation very upsetting and longed for how it used to be.

Making small and big changes easier

There are some ways in which I can make changes less difficult depending on what type of change it is (big or small).

For most changes, **having a plan and advance notice** is really important to me. Having advance notice that there is going to be a small change can mean I cope absolutely fine instead of being debilitated and the change ruining an entire day.

Being informed in advance means I can work out how my day is going to be ahead of time rather than having to be flexible in the moment (something I really, really struggle with).

A positive example would be if a friend decides to text me the night before the day we had agreed to meet and wishes to rearrange the time it would not bother me very much. I would have enough time to decide how to restructure my day to accommodate this change.

A negative example would be if my friend sends me a text just a few hours before our meeting was due. I would feel very distressed. This is what happens:

Meeting a friend at a coffee shop (example)

I have been getting on with my day in the most efficient way to accommodate our planned meeting, having probably done some work before the meeting that I would not normally have done (as mentioned above, anything 'different' that I am doing in the day will affect everything else in the day. Seeing this friend was something different).

The meeting was scheduled to take place at 2pm in a local coffee shop. I have carefully thought about my plan for the day and had decided that I would walk to the coffee shop with my dog, therefore moving my dog's walk from the morning to later in the day, which meant I did not need to walk her in the morning (which is what I usually do). Instead I used the morning to do my work to make up for not being able to work at

2pm. Fundamentally, I would made some adjustments to my day to make things run efficiently and better.

At around 10am, my friend texts me, apologises, and asked whether we could meet another day instead. This caused me a lot of distress because, if I had known this further in advance, I would have walked my dog in the morning as I normally do! Now my routine had been disrupted and was now 'inefficient'.

I think that neurotypical people are a bit more flexible about things. They may be a little annoyed or disappointed, but not incredibly anxious and distressed. Their reactions are for different reasons to mine and my reactions are on a much larger scale.

The problem with lack of advance notice is that the change made affects 'Everything Else' and then there's a lot of uncertainty and disruption over Everything Else. For example, I had a weightlifting coach who preferred not to plan in advance what we would be doing in our sessions. Although intellectually I understood his reasons for this, I am not able to function this way. I found it incredibly difficult to plan my own weightlifting sessions that I would be doing alone the days before seeing him without knowing what it is that I would be doing with him. For example, there was little point doing very heavy squats and fatiguing my legs the day before if he wanted us to do heavy clean and jerks in our session. Heavy clean and jerks require fresh, strong legs! Similarly, I might eat differently at night depending on what sort of workout I am doing the next day. Sometimes my coach would come over and say, "I know you wanted to do [this] but I would like us to do [this] today". I really do need plans and to stick to them rather than have spontaneity and change. The changes that other people make hugely affect many of the things that I am doing, have done or am planning to do.

I have enormous difficulty doing the newspaper round because turning up and finding that the newspapers have not arrived are always 'out of the blue' moments. Whenever the newspapers are not there, I feel so distressed. I am never sure what to do:

- Do I just stand and wait at the shop?
- How long am I going to be waiting?
- What if I go home (which is very inconvenient and disruptive) having mentally rearranged my routine only to find that, as soon as I get home, the newspapers arrive, which means I then have to immediately go back to the shop and get them?

- What if I wait at the shop and end up waiting a whole hour or more and they still have not arrived?

I have physically been through all of the scenarios listed and all of them are anxiety-provoking. Each and every time the newspapers are late, all those questions go round in my head, but the answer never gets any clearer. My dad says if they are late, "well just don't do them", but then I don't get paid, so this is not a feasible solution.

It would be far easier if the night before I could be informed whether or not the newspapers were going to be on time the next day. But due to the nature of this particular job, this cannot really happen.

Although I love delivering the newspapers, the job requires a level of flexibility that I just do not have, so sometimes this job goes from being my favourite one to being my least favourite and the most stressful. However, clearly I must have learned to manage this problem otherwise I would have given up doing the newspaper round a long time ago!

I have learned to cope with this eventuality because I have learned to **accept** that sometimes the newspapers will be late and I have come to **expect** that sometimes my routine is going to be disrupted. **Accepting and expecting that there may be a change** helps me enough to mean that I can carry on with this job, but the stress I feel when the newspapers are late is still tremendous.

However, not doing the newspaper round and missing out on this very important part of my routine and the catalyst to start my day (as well as losing the money the job gives me – though this is actually less important) is worse than the newspapers occasionally arriving late. So at the moment I put up with the stress.

I have come up with a solution to cope with the newspapers being late at the weekend (I do the newspaper round 7 days a week) that I can just about tolerate – though not ideal and still annoying. For the weekend newspaper round, I have changed my routine so that I do the newspapers a bit later *after* I have either exercised or walked the dog. By the time I finish with either of these activities, my newspaper round is usually ready. It was very hard to change my routine but I managed.

(The reason I cannot use this solution during the week is because my weekdays are more hectic and I have more things to do, and also because – and this is a big reason – the roads are very quiet at the weekend, so the sensory input is not as overloaded and distressing as when I do the newspaper round on weekdays.

To summarise, there are 2 strategies I use for managing the late newspapers problem:

1) I have come to expect and accept that the newspapers will sometimes be late
2) I have permanently adjusted my routine as much possible to anticipate for the later arrival of newspapers.

The way that I cope with *bigger changes* is to make them more like *evolutions*.

Change	An act or process in which something becomes different
Evolution	A gradual or natural development of something

Sometimes people comment that I have made changes to my life. It always makes me a bit uncomfortable when people say that as I do not really consider that I have made many changes at all and because I try to always avoid making changes. I do not want other people pointing out to me changes they think I have made as that reminds me that a change might have occurred which in itself makes me feel anxious!

I would say that generally most of the changes that have taken place in my life happened because of other people. Any changes I cause myself normally occur over long periods of time rather than there being a specific choice or single moment. Differences of my own doing usually 'evolved' rather than 'changed'.

I cope with things evolving better than I cope with things changing because if something evolves rather than changes, the transition period is not as sharp and abrupt and may not even be felt:

There are some ways to make things feel less like change and more like an evolution so if you or someone you care about has difficulty with big changes, here are some suggestions:

- Make one small change at a time
- Carry out the change over a long period of time
- Keep as much the same as possible during the change
- Emphasise that one day things will go back to feeling 'normal' again and that life will once again be 'stable'

My sister moving out of home was not as big of a change as it could have been and I think this is because it evolved over a period of time. In the time leading up to her leaving home, she was already spending a large amount of time out of the house anyway (she spent a lot of time at her partner's house or she was out with her friends). Compare this to the situation had she always been at home every single night and then one day just decided to leave! The latter would have affected me much more. The outcome would be the same (she moved out), but one would be an evolution and one would be a change. Can you see the difference?

It helps a lot to know why something has happened. A lot of the time, changes (especially small ones) happen without any clear or communicated reason as to why. I have noticed that sometimes people do not communicate why a change has taken place because either:

1) they think the reason is obvious (but if you are autistic, reasons are not usually obvious)
2) they think the change is minor so it does not need to be discussed (but no change is really minor to someone like me). My life is so planned and such a great amount of thought has gone into every task that I am doing, that there will likely be some sort of effect or disturbance with every change.

It is also helpful for me to **know the positive outcomes of the change.** This can be the positive outcomes of the change shown in the bigger picture or, even better, the way this change is positively going to affect me. For example, imagine if the newspapers were permanently going to be delivered later. I would need to understand both why and consider the positive outcomes of this in order to be able to accept it. If I learned that the reason the newspapers were going to be delivered later was because the shop decided to change their supplier so that they got a better price or received better customer service, it would make sense and I would understand. I would also agree that this was a positive change for the shop. I would also like to think about how this change might positively affect me. I am personally not that way inclined but lots of people might be happy to have a bit more of a lie-in, for example! For me, a positive might be that the arrival time of the newspapers was going to be more consistent, meaning my routine will be disrupted less frequently. Another way I have learned to cope with change is to **live in the moment.** I understand that keeping things the same is an important way for me to feel less anxious. My experience of the 'now' is that it does not change. Something can only be different and changing if there is something to compare it with. When I'm living in the moment, life feels the same, still and constant.

If I am living in the moment then my reality looks like this:

But if I am thinking about the future or the past as well as what is 'now', then my reality is sub-divided like this:

The 'now' now has something to be compared with and comparisons tend to mean that there are differences which in turn cause me anxiety.

So to focus mostly on the present moment is really the least anxiety-provoking way for me to be.

Thinking mostly about the present has positives. It is actually the basis of Mindfulness, one of the most effective therapies for managing stress and anxiety.

I wish every single day could be exactly the same forever. When I am content and things are going well, I feel very stable and safe. Why would I want things to change? But a wise person once said, "The only predictable in life is that life changes." It makes me feel terrified.

People come in and out of our lives; they sometimes go out of our lives forever. Education does not last forever. Jobs do not last forever. The experiences we are having change all the time. Our own thoughts change all the time. Writing and editing this book has been hard because a piece of writing is only true for a moment in time and the next time I look at it my views might have changed. People change. People grow up. People move away. People have babies. People get married. People get old. People die. The people we were once very close to change and we might no longer be able to relate to them.

I try to **avoid coming face to face with change,** so, as mentioned above, my way of coping is that **I do not think or talk very much about the past or the future.**

I am not sure why, for example, someone would want to go to a school reunion. Even if I had enjoyed school (as you know, I hated it), I still think I would really dislike going to a school reunion! I often walk past my old schools but I just see them as brick and mortar. I have no attachment to them and try to forget the memories. I cannot relate to people wishing to go back and look at their old school or at the places they grew up in.

I do not really like having memories because they remind me that life has changed. I do not like looking at photos of the past and even listening to old songs has the tendency to make me think about how life was at the time I used to listen to those songs. For example, every time now that I hear Song X, I am reminded of being at college and about the subjects I was studying, the people I knew, the journey I used to take, etc.

Instead of making me feel happy (and college was quite a happy time for me), the memories just remind me of all the changes that have since occurred. I just prefer not to come face to face with change. If I do not think about college, Song X, see photos from that time (I do not even like to keep items in my house that other people would probably consider mementos!) then I do not have to be so sharply reminded of changes that have taken place since.

People will not hear me reminiscing. I feel OK talking and thinking about the recent past or very near future, but periods of time that are further away make me uncomfortable. If I am to talk and think about the distant past then I only really like to talk and think about specific situations in a factual way. For example, I could think and talk about a specific assignment I did whilst at college or factually describe someone that I used to know. However, thinking about how life was holistically whilst I was at college (my sister was still living at home, my cats were alive, my granddad was alive, I was doing an extracurricular personal training course, I had some friends who I have no contact with now…), is unsettling. I just get too emotionally affected.

Comfortable ways of talking and thinking about the past	Uncomfortable ways of talking and thinking about the past
• **Factually** • **Specific situations only** • **Recent past only**	• **Emotionally** • **As life was holistically at the time** • **Distant past**

Perhaps my dislike, anxiety and avoidance of change is largely to do with how perceptive and sensitive I am. If I was not so perceptive, I do not think I would notice how much something had changed. I think a lot of people do not remember the detail nor significance of things that have happened in their life because they are not as perceptive as I am, so change does not affect them in the same way. Similarly, if I was not so sensitive, I would not be so emotionally affected by situations.

Even when a customer on my newspaper round no longer requires their newspaper anymore I grieve for my old cycle route to their house, the way I had to fold the newspaper and manoeuvre my hands to put it inside the letter box, the way the dog next door used to bark, the type of flowers in their front garden, how the house fitted conveniently between the previous and next customer, etc.

Not thinking or talking much about the past is the way that I feel I can cope with change. I sometimes completely detach from a situation so that I can move forward without feeling scared and unstable. A lot of the time it is easier for me to detach myself entirely rather than go through the grieving process. If my only option to get over change is to either grieve or to detach myself then detachment can be the easiest.

Therefore, when a change happens, I will sometimes simply ignore the change. I will not think or talk about it further. It can make me appear cold to other people but it is the only way sometimes to cope with the stress of the change and to avoid any hurt that might follow. Detachment also stops me from ruminating over why and how a change happened (all part of the grieving process – I spend so much time ruminating over how and why whatever it is happened). Ruminating can be a very stressful part of having ASD. Detachment means that rumination is avoided.

I have been in long-term relationships that have ended and immediately after they end I will go looking for a new relationship with someone else without thinking any further about my previous relationship. It is not because I "got over" the person so quickly, it is because forgetting about them completely is the only way I can:

1) stop ruminating
2) stop hurting.

Detaching means there is no transition period at all because there is no 'Was':

How life is now

Summary of how I have learned to cope with small and big changes:

- Have advance notice of changes
- Make changes more evolutionary
- Live in the moment
- Learn or understand the reasons for the change
- Consider the benefits of the change
- Do not expose myself so directly to past/future experiences
- Detach completely

Changing people

Several years after leaving university I met up with one of my classmates who I had not had any contact with since. During university he had been quite close to me and was someone that I used to talk to and walk with. He was someone who was also a bit of an 'outsider'. The people who I seem to get close to most easily are usually outsiders. When we met up however, I was disappointed to see how much he had changed. He was not the same person that I remembered and it made me feel so unsettled and disconnected. He had changed in ways that meant he was no longer an outsider, whilst I still feel I am.

I have also seen photos and read updates from other university classmates who have moved abroad, got married, had children, etc. The fact that these major changes have happened makes me feel completely disconnected. Not only does it put me face to face with 'change' (how that university phase has passed and it highlights that we're all in a different phase now), it also reminds me that I am different from lots of people.

Perhaps one of the reasons that I feel change so strongly is that I do not change as much or as quickly as other people. I sometimes feel that I am living in a world in which everyone else has got older and moved on but I got left behind. I always wanted to play with dolls with my younger sister, even when we were older teenagers, but she grew out of that much earlier than I did.

My day to day life is pretty much the same as it was at the time of writing Asperger's and Me. I wake up, do my newspaper round, have breakfast and I go into my garage and do weightlifting. Then I do my work. My interests are still exactly the same – I like weightlifting, computers, reading and writing, listening to audio books, listening to rap music and writing rap lyrics. My dislikes are still the same – I dislike socialising, B.A.N.A.N.A.s[1], travelling, going out during the evening, etc. I still wear

the same clothes that I was wearing maybe 10 or 15 years ago (if I do find a new item of clothing that I like I buy multiple quantities so that they last years! I was once asked by someone what sort of clothes I liked and where I got my clothes from and I didn't really know what to say, it's just not something I think about or do!). My personality is the same – I am introverted, observant, thoughtful, scheduled.

Although I have developed some strategies for many of the difficulties and dislikes I have, they have not gone away. Just because I do things such as radio interviews, or attend conferences and exhibitions, it does not mean that they are easy or that I enjoy them. These sorts of situations are still as awful for me now as they would always have been; I just seem to be able to cope better.

If you would like to know where I would like to be in 5 or 10 years time,

---

1 I dislike them so much and I dislike the word too!

I am hoping that I will be doing the same things that I am doing now, just doing them a bit more efficiently and successfully! I hope that I know the same people and that my relationships with them are still the same (they probably will not be, the university classmate example is proof of this, but it upsets me too much to think differently, so I focus on how things are now and not how they are going to be in the future...).

So some of the most unsettling relationships I have had are with people who change in ways which mean I no longer relate to them, such as my university classmate. Lots of the people I was once close to were also outsiders like me, people who were also a bit different. Finding out that they are no longer outsiders, i.e. because they now seem to have 'normal' lives or have started doing normal things in normal ways disconnects me from them. A friend described it as like "losing someone because they became 'normal', and I got left behind".

I like all sorts of people, ranging from the most quirky, to people who are very normal, but with people who are very normal it is much easier for me to know them if they are 'already normal' as opposed to knowing them and then they later 'become normal'.

What do I mean by 'normal'?

'Normal' can be described as doing conventional activities or having conventional goals in life such as having romantic or sexual feelings, being in a relationship, getting married, starting a family, moving away from home, getting a good job, working a 9-5, making money, travelling, having a strong social life, having varied or conventional interests and both achieving and participating in them through typical ways.

My own thinking is that you can be normal without being neurotypical and just because you are neurotypical it does not make you normal.

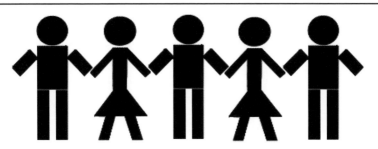

'Normal' neurotypical people.

One 'outsider' neurotypical person + four 'normal' neurotypical people.

An 'outsider' neurotypical person becoming 'normal'.

Therefore, one of the reasons I get on better with people who are a lot older than me is because – unless they are natural outsiders – they are far more likely to already be normal. I suspect that most people who were going to become normal would be most likely to do so before they were 30. The university classmate has now got a normal life – he has travelled, moved out of his parents' home, has a good job, has friends, earns money, is married, etc. At the time I met up with him he told me that he had temporarily moved back in with his parents but now disliked the situation, which I found hard to relate to, because I am very close to my family and because I still feel like a child and because when I knew him he was also a childlike person who needed his parents. Learning that he had grown up and become 'normal' made me unsettled as he was not like this at university. At university, he spent most time alone at home like me, studying or doing his sport (his was golf, mine was weightlifting). He now no longer makes playing golf any sort of priority and rarely plays.

I remember my first relationship. I was dating a young man who was very, very shy and quiet like me, and liked being at home on the computer also like me. He was an outsider. However, once he went to university, he became very sociable and outgoing and he became normal. Our relationship did not work out and I remember feeling so upset because he had "changed".

Being friends with people who are older than me has helped me so

26

much because all of my older friends are much more consistent and stable, both in personality and lifestyle. If they are already 'normal', that is cool. But if they are not normal by now then they are probably never going to be! It is the change of people I find unsettling, rather than what they are like. I have one older friend, who I had not seen or spoken to for several years, text me asking to meet up. I really wanted to see her but I was anxious that she might be different from how I remembered. I did not want to repeat the university classmate situation. I then texted another friend (who I am in touch with much more frequently) who is a mutual friend. I texted her <I'm anxious about seeing her> She texted back <Don't worry. She'll not have changed> It was nice that she knew me so well that she already sensed why I was anxious! She was right too; I saw my friend and she had not changed.

One of my friends, who is the same age as me and who also has ASD, has been a great comfort to me because he is the only person I know who has remained the same for all the years I have known him. He once sent me a text that said <You can always be sure that I am still the same person. Not going anywhere. Not doing anything different. I don't change>. This message is one of the most lovely and most comforting things a person could say to me. Other people might like the words "I love you", but **I like to hear and be reminded that someone has not changed.**

The only other strategy I use to cope with those who might have changed is **to not see them** if I realise or strongly suspect that they have changed so much that I will no longer feel close to them. This is probably a form of detachment. I am certain, for example, that I would not want to meet up with any of my other university classmates. I can see on social media and from the occasional text message the different lifestyles they are now leading.

If the period of time between the last and the next meeting has been very long, I need to be very **careful in deciding whether or not I will go and meet the person.** A person who has significantly changed will leave me feeling very, very disconnected and upset.

Summary of how I have learned to cope with changing people:

- Have friendships with older people
- Make friends with people who are already 'outsiders'
- Be careful about meeting people who I have not seen or
- spoken to for a long time – I can try to do some 'detective work' in advance to determine whether or not they are likely to have 'changed', before agreeing to meet

WHAT i HAVE LEARNED ABOUT ROUTINE

Flexible Time
Alone Time
Boxes
Hyperfocus Time
Physical activity
Getting a dog
Big, out of routine activities

My routine is one of the most important things to me. The routine being of such high importance is what makes me know I am different.

The activities I like to follow are those within my routine and my daily goal is to follow my routine. I have quite a strict morning and evening routine that I need to follow, but I have learned to **make my daytimes more flexible.**

The way I plan my day and week, and the ability to follow through with my plan, is so important to my mental well-being. I use routine to ensure that I have enough 'social energy' (more on this topic later), to keep my anxiety down, and to ensure that everything runs as efficiently as possible. It's important to me that my life is run efficiently because it means my executive function works better (more about this also later).

I have learned the importance of **doing tasks early in the day.** I like tasks to be completed sooner rather than later because I do not like having anything outstanding (you know that I like to tick boxes and I like to tick them fast!). When I was at college and university, I used to dread timetables which had late lessons. The worst timetable was when the whole day was empty up until 3pm and then at 3-5pm there was a lecture. I felt so agitated all the time up to 3pm because there was still this big task 'outstanding' and I could not relax until it was over. I will say

29

however, that I am now far better at coping with activities that occur later in the day than I used to be. This is because I am now far more capable of **living in the moment.** I do not worry so much about what is coming up because I am too focused on what I am doing now. It also definitely helps that **each day I am doing lots of activities that I really enjoy.**

Flexible Time

Although I have quite a rigid routine, I have learned to make it more flexible to accommodate disturbances caused by outside factors.

I have learned to be a bit more flexible about times. There is now some degree of **timing flexibility for the start and end times** of the newspaper round, weightlifting and walking the dog (because weightlifting and walking the dog depend on the newspaper round and the newspaper round can be unreliable). For example, planning to do weightlifting "some time" "around" 7am or 7.30am makes me far less anxious than planning to do it at "exactly" 7am.

People sometimes think I am "controlling". I am controlling, but I do not intend to be controlling of other people, rather I am trying to control *my own world* and desperately trying hard to create some sort of predictability and sameness. The problem is, when other people are involved (because we are in the 'shared world'), they feel as though I am controlling *them.* I am trying to control the situation rather than the person.

For example, say I have planned to meet up with a friend "at 3pm" and they are 10 minutes late. I will be anxious because they are late and, if it is someone I know well, I will probably be cross with them too. We may end up having an argument because I pointed out and became upset at them being 10 minutes late and they then call me "controlling." But to me, I planned *my whole day* to accommodate that meeting. Having a set time to meet was one way of me trying to have some structure to my day. I was trying to control my own day, not control them.

If friends turning up late is a common occurrence that happens to you and causes you distress, then my strategy for dealing with this is to **arrange to meet people between a time frame as opposed to at a specific time.** Even if you have agreed 3pm, in your head it might be helpful to think of the meeting as happening "some time between 2.50pm and 3.10pm". It enables you to still have your rigid schedule as well as giving the other person a bit of flexibility.

(Perhaps another reason why I choose to be alone so much is because it protects me from all the spontaneity and change that other people cause!) Similarly, when I book an appointment to see the GP, even though the appointment time might be 10.45am, in my head I might consider it "some time between 10.45am and 11.15am". If I have the expectation that the time is going to be different from what it is supposed to be I feel less anxious about what the time is.

Something that has helped me is to **have sections of 'flexible time' as part of my day** that can be used for anything outside of my normal activities. You can see from my schedule that a large proportion of my day is made up of Flexible Time. This time normally ends up being used for work but it can also be used differently, usually for things such as going shopping, going to the bank, having meetings, seeing my friends and anything else that might need doing that I had not planned for. Since I have already planned in Flexible Time for doing 'other tasks', then doing these other tasks is not as disruptive as if I had not planned in Flexible Time from the start. I do not think it is a good idea to have my whole day completely full of tasks and set times, as the spontaneity of daily life does mean that on occasion, tasks will have to be added, taken out, moved, etc. If I have got a dedicated gap in my routine allocated for this sort of change then it does not cause me as much stress.

I must say that **being self-employed has helped me** enormously, as I have got the ability to change my day around if I need to and, apart from meals and my morning and evening activities, nothing else actually *has* to be done. I don't have to be anywhere at any particular time. I don't have to stay anywhere for any length of time. Being self-employed means that I can actually do anything at more or less any time. I fit all my work into any of the Flexible Time slots of my day and get on with it at my own pace.

Alis's Daily Routine	
Starting time of task	**Task**
4am	**Wake up***
5-5.45am	**Newspaper round***
6-6.30am	**Breakfast***
6.15-6.45am	**Work***
7-7.30am	**Weightlifting***
8-8.30am	**Walk the dog***
9-9.30am	**Flexible Time**
12-12.30pm	**Lunch***
12.15-12.45pm	**Flexible Time**
5pm	**Dinner***
5.15pm	**Work***
6-6.30pm	**Time to recharge**
9-9.30pm	**Sleep***
Tasks that are essential to be done at those times	

I try to arrange everything so that it fits inside my routine. Usually, if something can be fitted into my routine it will be the difference between me doing something and not doing it at all. For example, if somebody wants to see me late in the evening I will almost certainly not be able to go. However, I would be able to see them if it was earlier in the day inside Flexible Time.

Alone Time

I have to have lots of Alone Time every day. My routine incorporates time alone throughout the day, including the evening. Alone Time has lots of benefits, including allowing me to recharge and 'hyperfocus'.

Because of the way in which my days are currently set up, I am alone most of the time anyway. However, any day in which I am doing something 'different', 'big' or 'new', I will definitely need to **have frequent breaks in order to be alone**. For example, if I am out most of the day at an exhibition, I will need lots of breaks in order to go outside and be on my own.

I always knew that I needed, or wanted, more time alone than most people, but I have not always truly understood the significance of having it, and the consequences of not having it. When I do not get enough Alone Time it affects everything.

Not only do I have ASD, I am also an introvert, so Alone Time is what gives me energy. Without enough time alone, my everyday state is 'depleted' in energy. It is very hard and very stressful going out into the world every day in a depleted state. I feel like I cannot, and do not, fulfil my potential; and everything I do is far more stressful and less enjoyable than it otherwise would be.

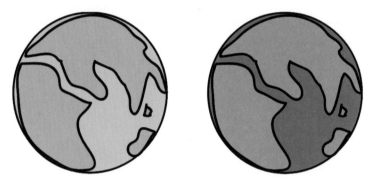

Feeling depleted means the world appears dull and grey rather than blue and green.

Even doing activities that ought to be fun, such as my weightlifting, become challenging when I am 'depleted'.

Another problem that comes from being depleted is that social interaction is more difficult. When I am tired, it might not even be that I do not talk as much, it can actually be that I say things I do not want to say, things that I do not mean, and start having to 'mask' (more about masking later). I will mask because I do not have the energy to work out how to say what I want, in the best manner, and that tends to mean that I just give an easy, generic response like being on autopilot, or no response at all. Remember that when you have ASD, your thoughts and feelings are different to others, so it can often require moderation and consideration before saying them out loud.

When I am in a depleted state, seeing my friends and maintaining my relationships becomes difficult. Even the people I like and ought to want to see, I now try to avoid. I cannot enjoy my relationships when I am so exhausted.

One of the reasons I believe that I had so much trouble having relationships when I was younger was because I was too exhausted all of the time (the reality is that it is only since having a flexible working life that I have been able to achieve the amount of Alone Time that I truly need). Anyone who tried to be nice to me or include me in social activities just made me feel stressed.

Even if I wanted to see or talk to someone, in the past I was always hindered by my lack of energy. In a lot of cases I made the mistake of ignoring my exhaustion and deciding to go and be sociable anyway – and of course this just left me feeling even more exhausted.

I remember dating or seeing friends at weekends, because I felt I *should* have had the energy to do things like this and because everyone else seemed to spend their weekend with their friends and family. Why didn't I? However, me spending my weekend socialising wasn't sensible as it meant there was not enough Alone Time for me to recharge myself for the following Monday when school, university or work would begin again. This meant that the following working week was now even more tiring and stressful.

The funny thing is that I vividly remember the thoughts I had during these times. I would think to myself, "How does everyone else have so much energy to do things at weekends? I'm exhausted!" I had this strong urge to have the weekends to myself. I was so desperate for that time alone. Now I understand why.

For autistic people, **time for them to recharge** is very important. How it is defined and how an individual chooses to recharge themselves will depend on the individual. Time to recharge, for me, is **time in which I am alone but it is also time in which I do not have anything particular left to do** (all boxes have been ticked), because only when there is nothing left to do can I relax. It is time when I no longer have to be 'on'. This time allows me to recover from the stresses of daily life. My most effective time to recharge occurs in the evening. Whenever I have to do activities that are outside my usual routine, I do them in the daytime and try to do them as early as possible. Doing an activity in the evening would consume my recharge time. It will mean that I have to be 'on' for too long. Doing activities sooner rather than later means I can be 'off' sooner.

What is 'on'?

'On' is that feeling of alertness I have and pressure that I experience when there is something I ought to be doing, or when there are other people around me. Even if the people around me are quiet and getting on with their own activities, I am still very alert *just in case* they talk to me.

Being 'on' is actually a feeling of anxiety.

Boxes

'Boxes' are *all the tasks that I need to do in a day.* For me, the main 'boxes' to be ticked include the newspaper round, weightlifting and walking the dog. These are the tasks that *have* to be done. Because I am self-employed, 'work' can really be done when it is convenient for me and nothing is ever really urgent. I do not have a fast-paced or deadline-orientated job. Boxes can be moved around to other times or days.

My routine facilitates my need for all **boxes to be ticked as soon as possible.** Wanting to complete tasks quickly is just the way that I am and, throughout the day, my thoughts primarily revolve around "What boxes do I have left?" and "How quickly can I tick them?" There are some positives to being this way as well as some negatives.

Now I will demonstrate an example of how I can sometimes struggle to manage boxes in daily life when I am doing something 'different' in the day:

Positives	Negatives
I don't forget things	I'm always in a rush
I get things done	If something is starting or finishing late, I get very agitated
I always finish what I start	I am pre-occupied by what time it is
I always have my evenings off	It can sometimes distract me from the present moment
I'm known as being reliable and dependable	I can't leave anything unfinished

The positives and negatives of being someone who always needs to be 'ticking boxes'.

Newspaper round followed by weightlifting followed by an exhibition example

I have a 'different' sort of day to deal with. I am attending an exhibition. I have planned to:

1) do the newspaper round
2) do my weightlifting
3) hurry off to attend the exhibition

These are all my 'boxes' and I am keen to make sure that they are all done and that they are done quickly. I am keen to get home having done all these tasks so that I can feel content that all boxes are ticked allowing me time to recharge. My plan is realistic, feasible and enables me to cope with the different day I am having.

5am → Box 1: Newspaper round
7am → Box 2: Weightlifting
9am → Box 3: Exhibition
3pm → Time to recharge

A problem arises when I go to collect my newspapers and they are either not there or are late and the shopkeeper says to me that he is not sure what time they are going to arrive.

At this point, Option One is to wait for the newspapers to arrive and hope they come soon, but if they do not come soon and I have to wait even longer then I have to accept that I will not have time to do weightlifting. This still means that I will manage to get to the exhibition but will miss weightlifting. I will now have an agitated feeling that something is 'wrong' for the rest of the day. Then I feel very distracted throughout the exhibition and contemplate doing weightlifting after the exhibition when I get home (just so I can tick the box). However, throughout the exhibition, because the weightlifting box is currently unticked, I feel agitated and this preoccupies my thoughts. I would always rather *not* do weightlifting when it is later in the day because:

1) doing it too late means it consumes my recharging time (weightlifting for me is not strictly time for recharging because to do it I have to be 'on')
2) all the time leading up to when I get to do my weightlifting I will feel agitated, restless, excited, unsettled, etc.

Option Two is to decide not to do the newspaper round at all and to do my weightlifting instead, followed by attending the exhibition. I will not be able to do the newspaper round later after the exhibition, so I will have that agitated feeling because I did not tick the newspaper round box and then the whole day feels 'wrong'.

Both options, of missing weightlifting or missing the newspaper round, will leave me feeling unsettled throughout the day and it means I find it hard to relax and recharge.

Option Three is to decide in advance that the whole day is going to be a 'write off', which means that I decide I am going to have a day off weightlifting and cancel doing the newspaper round so that the only box there will be on this particular day is the exhibition. **I sometimes choose to have days like this that I write-off** because they take away any pressure to tick boxes and allow me to be more flexible which all in all mean that I feel less agitated. I call these days my Write-Off Days or Non-Routine Days.

I have noticed that one difference between myself and most people I know is that they appear to have a vague idea of what they want to achieve on any given day, but the actual timings and way in which those things are achieved are often a bit 'rough' and they do not necessarily become preoccupied by how much time to recharge they are going to have available (this is because time to recharge is not needed for people in the same way that it is for me).

Lots of people do not even seem to mind if a task does not get done! Sometimes they do not even mind if none of the tasks planned get done because they just think, "Oh well, I will do it tomorrow instead". The thought of having a list of boxes to be ticked and then getting to the end of the day having ticked none of them fills me with terror!

COMPLETING WHAT I PLANNED TO DO IS REALLY IMPORTANT. IF I DO NOT MANAGE TO ACHIEVE WHAT I HAVE SET OUT TO DO, I FEEL REALLY AGITATED. FEELING AGITATED AFFECTS THE VERY IMPORTANT TIME TO RECHARGE

I am really rigid with regards to *when* and *how* things are done. I always say that the rigidity relating to my routine is one of the most debilitating aspects of my ASD, but it is also one of the most helpful and empowering. I now know that it is *because* of my routine and adherence to rigid schedules that I function as well as I do. I am very capable and productive in my day to day life, and this is largely because I have created a structure that acts to facilitate me. It is restrictive, but it also enables me to achieve wonderful things.

Hyperfocus Time

One of the reasons I need so much time alone is that **it is important that I am disrupted as little as possible throughout the day,** so that I can: 1) do everything quickly and well, and 2) get tasks finished. In order to do this I go into a state of 'hyperfocus' (deep concentration). It is a brilliant skill to have. Hyperfocus is a core part of who I am and it is time that I actually crave. When I am hyperfocusing, I have very little awareness of anything else apart from the task that I am doing. However, it is not easy to get into this state and interruptions can very easily take me out of it. **I have made my life flexible to accommodate disturbances** but I do not expect that to be the norm. **I still need most of my time to be uninterrupted.**

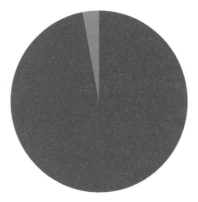

I crave being able to hyperfocus which is why I often need to be left alone. I

■ **Task that I am doing**   ■ **Anything else**

am lucky that there is no one else at home (where I work) during the daytime, however, when somebody else is at home, I kindly **ask them not to disturb me** or I will put a 'do not disturb' sign on the door and I will take it off when I have finished what I am doing. People who know me understand that they will not get an immediate response if they text or instant message me. I let people know that I will only ever respond once I am finished with the task that I am currently focused on, even if my phone or computer are right in front of me.

It makes me very, very irritable if I am pulled out of my hyperfocus state before I am ready. I wish people would not interrupt me so much – for their sake as well as mine! I do not want to be irritable with people – I would much rather be friendly and helpful – but if someone catches me at the wrong moment, I am likely to be irritable!

I dislike being phoned out the blue and will always try not to answer, the exception being my gran, who I of course love and worry about, so I will always pick up, even if it does make me irritable. It annoys me when somebody phones me and then sends an email saying that they "tried to call but could not get through". I always think, well, why do they expect me to just be available on demand? The only explanation must be that they think they are calling a generic reception number… Phone calls for me have to be planned otherwise they are an interruption.

The doorbell ringing is another irritating interruption. It rings a lot at my house and 9 out of 10 times it will be a courier delivery (so I probably ought to answer!). The noise of the ring is shrill and hurts my ears, but the worst thing is the unpredictability and suddenness. If I have planned to have some undisturbed time, so that I can hyperfocus, then I have not planned to be having to answer the door. Even if I choose not to answer the door (which I sometimes do if I am hyperfocusing), the noise is still an interruption. One way to reduce the likelihood of being interrupted by couriers is that I leave a note on the front door asking them to leave parcels in the front garden (but usually they ignore the note and ring the doorbell anyway).

A strong need to hyperfocus is perhaps something else that is related to being autistic. I am not sure neurotypical people - even when they are concentrating - are bothered by being interrupted as much as I am. Perhaps they do not need as much undisturbed time? This explains why it is the norm that people work in shared spaces that are busy and chaotic. Or perhaps most people just have better ability to get back on track with what they are doing after they have been interrupted? Perhaps most people just do not have the trait of being able to hyperfocus, or maybe their version of concentrating deeply is different to my state of hyperfocus?

With ASD, there are also often the additional difficulties linked to executive function such as: 1) being able to start a task, and 2) switching between tasks. Therefore interrupting someone autistic who is getting on well with what they are doing could be a greater upheaval than for a neurotypical person. My neurotypical friends and colleagues seem far less affected by interruptions than I am, in terms of their work and daily activities generally.

I also have problems switching from being in

hyperfocus to 'normal state'. It takes me about a minute to do this (by this time, the aforementioned couriers have often given up and gone away!).

I get hugely irritated and upset if I am interrupted so much that it ruins the time to hyperfocus that I have set aside. It is not an easy state to get into, so to be pulled out of it, before I have finished what I am doing, often means I will not be able to get back into the hyperfocus state.

Having **a life of minimal tasks and responsibilities** works best for me because it means that I am likely to have enough opportunities for any tasks that require me to hyperfocus. I generally try to make sure that **any task I do is brief** so that I can hyperfocus and get it finished before a disturbance has a chance to occur. I have become really good at breaking tasks down into much smaller ones and **I do one small task at a time.** For each small task I can hyperfocus. It is unrealistic for me to expect to be able to hyperfocus on a large task that takes several hours (there are too many other things I need to do and too many people who need to talk to me throughout the day!), but it is realistic for me to be able to hyperfocus on something that perhaps takes 15 to 60 minutes. Occasionally I will disappear off to my bedroom (where there is no internet connection, no telephone and where the doorbell cannot be heard as loudly) for a few hours to complete a large task but this is not often. It is not practical for me to do this on a regular basis.

I am also careful about *when* I plan to hyperfocus on a task. There is no point planning to hyperfocus if I have got to do something else soon afterwards (deadlines are a hyperfocus killer). For example, I never begin a task that requires hyperfocus before I am about go in the gym or have lunch. My ability to hyperfocus is definitely better on the days when I have fewer things to do.

Although hyperfocus cannot be forced, I have learned that there are optimal conditions for it to be successful:

- No interruptions
- A task that is brief
- No other task scheduled in (or *directly* afterwards)

Physical activity

Another part of my routine that is helpful is **doing physical exercise in the morning.** Physical exercise is very important (and means more than just ticking a box!). I always have lots of physical energy when I wake up and I need to burn it off, otherwise I feel too agitated, restless and unable to focus mentally. My intuition tells me that my mind works best when my body is tired and blood is rushing round the body and to the brain. Anxiety is also a form of energy and so doing exercise helps burn off some of that energy leaving me feeling less anxious (I always feel a bit anxious, it is my normal feeling, but exercise makes it a bit less).

Physical activity also helps me sleep much better, so I have consistent and higher quality sleep (which also contributes hugely to feeling better generally).

Getting a dog

The main thing that changed in my life is that we got a dog! So I have had to change my routine a little (a lot!) to accommodate her. **I coped with getting a dog by making her daily walk a part of my routine.** It is lovely walking her in the morning and it is healthy exercise. I used to walk my dog after doing weightlifting. This was part of the daily agenda up until summer 2017:

How the time of my weightlifting time was suddenly changed example

One morning I was in my weightlifting room doing weightlifting. I normally lift at around 7am but it was a bit later on this particular day, around 10am, and there was a knock on the wall. I looked out the window and saw a lady standing outside. I opened the door and the conversation went like this:

"Hi! Do you mind me asking… what's that noise?" she said.

"I do Olympic weightlifting," I replied.

"Oh… right. Well, we hear it every day. It goes on every day at about 7am."

"Yes," I said.

I was not sure what she meant by this comment. She was making a statement, not asking a question.

"But it goes on every single day," she continued.

This comment confused me. In my mind, I always thought it was an excellent thing to be exercising every day. The human body needs daily exercise.

"Yes, I do weightlifting every day," I said.

I was still not entirely sure why we were having this conversation.

"It's quite loud," she said eventually.

I was still not sure what she was implying. She had not been very clear. Then it clicked with me that perhaps the noise had been waking her up too early.

"Sorry," I said. "Is there a better time for me to do weightlifting?"

"Err, well, after 9 o' clock," she replied.

This was the start of a massive change in routine for me as it seemed that from now on I would never be able to do weightlifting before 9am again.

For some people, it might not be such an issue to move their exercise time, but it was really a very big issue for me. My body physically performs exercise best early in the morning because I have most energy. I am someone who never wakes up tired. Every day I wake up and I am raring to go! Because of this and because I am athletic, I feel that I have the best workouts early in the morning. I lift more weight, I feel more motivated and my technique is far sharper. I feel that my performance is optimal at that time. As the day goes on I feel that my physical and mental energy decreases. So the later the time in the day that I lift, the less energy I have available. This might not have been such a problem if I was just a casual weightlifter, but I am not. I take a professional approach to my weightlifting and it is also my special interest so I want to dedicate myself fully.

I also have that issue of "well I *could* do weightlifting later in the day, but this would mean there is an 'outstanding box' waiting to be ticked", and all the time leading up to it, whilst this box is unticked, I would feel agitated.

After the conversation with the neighbour I had to swap the times for weightlifting and walking my dog. Weightlifting had to happen at around 9am rather than 7am, and walking my dog had to happen at 7am rather than 8am. There were two main consequences of doing this:

1) there is now less mental and physical energy available for weightlifting
2) I have lost touch with the friends with whom I used to socialise because we used to walk the dogs together at 8am.

Losing touch with friends has been quite significant. I do not make friends easily and, like many people on the autistic spectrum, I struggle greatly with unstructured social interaction. Socialising with people whilst walking the dogs together was a nice, structured activity. I knew what time we were meeting, the route we would take, what time it would end and I knew when and how we would meet up again. The dogs had fun. Conversation could revolve around the dogs, the park, and the wildlife in the park or general local gossip. The situations were very predictable as they were always the same. Sadly now this has stopped. My friends are not early birds like I am or it seems it is not practical for them to go out walking at 7am, so I no longer see them.

Neurotypical people might just think, "Well, why does Alis not arrange to see them another time or go to see them and do something else?" When you have ASD however, it is not that straightforward. It is very hard for me to see my dog walking friends in a different setting, at different times and even just working out whether and how to arrange all of this is far too confusing and complicated. How do I even know they will want to see me in a different setting, for example?

Seeing my dog walking friends when we are not dog walking feels different, out of context and it is not as convenient. Socialising is also not ideally what I want to use my Flexible Time for, as it causes me anxiety.

For the first few months of this new arrangement I really missed my dog walking friends. I went through that intense grieving process for how things were before the neighbour knocked on my wall and changed my routine for the foreseeable future. I am used to it now, but it is been really hard and I have lost the social network I used to have. I used to meet some lovely people whilst on my dog walks. When I am walking at 7am, the park is empty.

This is an example of how everything in my day is very carefully scheduled. No task is included that does not have to be there. Everything has been thought through very carefully to ensure the most efficient results. **If activities are efficient, they are more enjoyable** (I will talk about it more later, but when you have executive function impairments, making something as easy and as convenient as possible is key to not only ensuring that something actually gets done, but also to how much enjoyment you will gain from it).

One of the reasons walking dogs with my friends was so enjoyable was because it was convenient and easy – the dogs need to be walked anyway, the route is set, the time is set and it is fitting inside my normal routine. Because all those factors were taken care of I found I could actually relax and have a bit more energy available to enjoy the socialising.

Occasionally I go walking with my dog walking friends later during Flexible Time, but it is not on a regular basis because I am usually working. I risk doing weightlifting at 7am occasionally but I find it hard to focus because I worry that I am disturbing someone (and then if I am not focused 100% during weightlifting it can be very dangerous).

By the time I finished writing this book, I had reconstructed my weightlifting room completely to include sound proofing.

Big, out of routine activities

I have learned that I get very tired quickly when I have to do things outside of my routine. I find I get stuck in a repetitive cycle when I am tired as the exhaustion means it is even harder to get back on track with my routine. Additionally, not following my routine is one of most common triggers for feelings of sadness. Too much sadness too often makes me feel depressed:

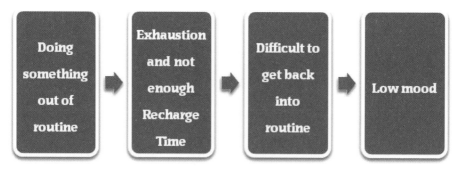

This is why it is important for me to:

1) have the Flexible Time periods in the day because then I can do something different but, since it still means I am following my routine, I do not get as tired

2) keep my evenings free
3) make sure I have enough time alone every day.

If I have to do something different that takes up such a large part of the day, and consumes periods that are not Flexible Time, I plan and prepare for the likely consequences of being exhausted. On the days that I go to an exhibition for example, if I cannot get straight back into my routine the following day, I will plan for the following day to be a 'write-off' and just full of empty time so that I can recharge. **I will never do more than one day in a row of big non-routine activities.**

I think a large reason why I have previously had so much depression and burnout is because my routine was being interrupted, without enough time to recover from the disruption:

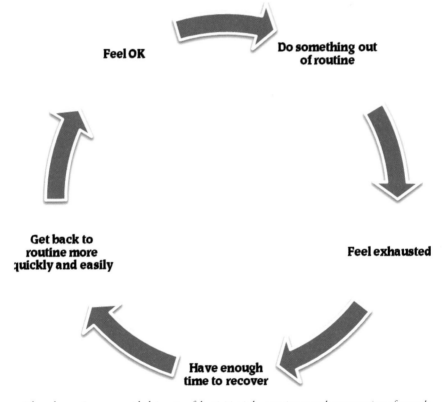

Feel OK

Do something out
of routine

Feel exhausted

Have enough
time to recover

Get back to
routine more
quickly and easily

The only way I can cope with doing stressful activities is by ensuring enough recovery time afterwards. Only when I have recovered enough will I be able to cope with doing another stressful activity.

It is essential for me to make sure that **I have enough time to recharge after doing something non-routine or that involves social activity** so that I can recover my energy and quickly get back into my routine. This is one of the ways that I cope with life.

Summary of how I have achieved a successful routine:

- Have 'sections' in the day to do things rather than specific times (for example, instead of me aiming to do weightlifting at *exactly* 7am, I will try to do it *sometime between* 7am and 7.30am, which allows for any delay to the newspaper round)
- Allocate periods of Flexible Time in the day
- Do things early in the day
- Keep the number of boxes to be ticked daily to a minimum
- Have a daily plan that facilitates getting tasks done (so nothing is left outstanding)
- Spend most of my day being on my own
- Keep evenings free so that time to recharge is available
- Ensure breaks throughout the day to have time alone
- Ask people not to interrupt, or ask them to have patience, instead of expecting an immediate response
- Arrange circumstances so that hyperfocus can be achieved
- Have a strict morning and evening routine but be more flexible during the day
- Be active in the morning
- Make sure I get enough recharge time when I do something that is stressful or that is not a normal part of my routine
- Deliberately plan for certain days to be Write-Off Days

WHAT i HAVE LEARNED ABOUT ANXIETY

The Freeze response
Being at home or on my own
Having choice
Living in the moment
Mental energy
Constants
Imagining situations
Familiarising feelings
Doing things immediately
Pinpointing triggers
Structured and planned situations
Exercise, nutrition and sleep

I was not sure whether to have a chapter about anxiety because the feelings of anxiety are all encompassing and affect every aspect of my life. However, I have decided to include some general strategies that help me feel less anxious which do not fit conveniently into the other chapters.

'Anxiety is an unpleasant feeling that we all experience at times. It is a word often used to describe when we feel 'uptight', 'irritable', 'nervous', 'tense', or 'wound up'[2]

I did not always know what anxiety was and that feeling anxious all the time was not what everybody else might be feeling. A few times in the past I have been worried by how much I was sweating. I went to the GP about my problem and had some tests. There was nothing wrong with me. Several years later I now recognise that the symptoms were caused by anxiety.

2 Bourne, E. (2005). Anxiety: Moodjuice self-help guide. Available: http://www.moodjuice.scot.nhs.uk/anxiety. asp. Last accessed 28th Oct 2018.

Now I understand that my normal feeling is that of being anxious.

> *I WOULD LOVE FOR PEOPLE TO LEARN, OR TO EDUCATE THEIR LOVED ONES, ABOUT WHAT ANXIETY IS AND WHAT IT FEELS LIKE, AND TO HIGHLIGHT THAT IT IS NOT NORMAL FOR A PERSON TO FEEL EXPERIENCE ANXIETY ALL THE TIME*

Anxiety is very tiring. I am sure an anxious person gets more tired than a person who does not have an anxiety problem. A person who is anxious is close to the fight-flight-freeze state a lot of the time. To me this means having excess energy or anxiety at the surface:

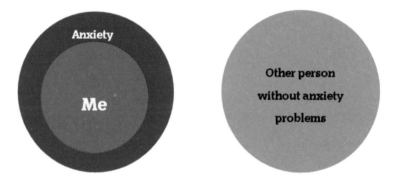

If someone spends the majority of their life feeling like this, is it any wonder that they:

1) feel tired and need a lot of time to recharge
2) struggle to focus in normal situations, let alone achieve their potential in work and education
3) struggle to enjoy any extracurricular activities.

Having anxiety affects my overall experience and enjoyment of life. Just as having low social energy causes me to feel 'depleted' so does lots of anxiety. Life is dull and grey rather than blue and green. It means that normal things are more stressful for me than for the average person, and it often means that activities that ought to be enjoyable are over shadowed by the feeling of anxiety. That is why it is so important for an anxious person to find ways to bring that anxiety down. Here are some of the things I have learned about what makes me anxious and how to cope with anxiety.

The Freeze response

Fight, Flight and Freeze are three common responses to anxiety. The 'Freeze' response is interesting. There is probably less known about this response than the fight and flight responses. With me, I most often experience the Freeze response when faced with a situation that I did not expect to encounter. I can actually feel myself freezing.

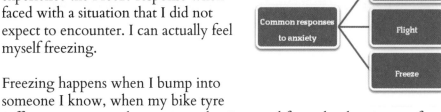

Freezing happens when I bump into someone I know, when my bike tyre suffers a puncture, when an item that I wanted from the shop is out of stock... and even when a park gate is locked. Here's a good example of the last one:

The locked park gate example

My routine was: walking my dog along the river which connects to the adjacent park via a gate. I would walk along the river, go through the gate and come home again through the park. There was one time when I got to the gate and it was locked! I was so confused and startled that I just stood there completely frozen because it was completely unexpected.

Neurotypical people will be able to relate to the freeze response because it is what happens to many people when they are shocked or scared. In that moment, they cannot think rationally. The difference is however, that neurotypical have these moments much less frequently. Autistic people are likely to have these moments more often because:

1) they feel anxious most of the time, even in normal everyday situations
2) they have so much difficulty with flexible thinking (which means they have trouble knowing what to do when a situation happens that they did not expect).

I never want to just bump into someone that I know or for them to come to my house to surprise me. I once had a friend, who I had not seen for many years, come over to my house without any warning of the visit. He meant well, he wanted to surprise me and was very excited to see me and thought that I would be excited to see him, but the whole time I was completely frozen so this was not an occasion that I enjoyed. **Planned interactions are very important** for me, and ultimately for the other person, because then they will see me when I am feeling more relaxed.

A 2 minute chat at my front door just because a friend happens to be walking by and wants to say "hello" needs to be arranged, in exactly the same way that we would arrange to walk the dogs or meet for a cup of tea. A text from them even 5 minutes beforehand that says, <I am popping round in a moment> is enough to stop me from freezing which is what happens when they turn up out the blue.

I dislike answering the door anyway as I never know who it is and what their reason for knocking is. Should someone turn up at my door who I didn't expect, I will freeze. A good example is answering the door because I think it is the postman. I have prepared for it to be him and so I know what I am going to say and do. But if when I open the door it turns out to be a salesperson, because it is unexpected, I will freeze. Even if I know what to say (due to it being a 'social script' type of interaction) because I thought it was going to be the postman, I will be so anxious that I won't know what to say.

It is worse if it is a *friend* who turns up unexpectedly (some of my friends have a habit of knocking at my door just because they are in the area) because they *expect* me to engage in conversation. Salespeople and postmen are less concerned. My friends however, are likely *expecting* me to make small talk – but even if they are not – they are *expecting* me to be friendly, polite and to smile and express that I am happy to see them. It is not a situation that I find easy to cope with. It is very important to me that interaction is planned otherwise I cannot be the friendly, genuinely-interested-in-them person I would like to be.

Other solutions that I have come up with for dealing with the unexpected are all about anticipation – **anticipating things that could 'go wrong'.** For example, thinking in advance about what I am going to do if the item that I wish to buy in the shop is out of stock, or what I am going to do if the gate to the park is locked? I have built up a large 'database' in my head of alternative options. Sometimes an option can only be added to my database once it has been encountered because, due to difficulties with flexible thinking, it is usually extremely difficult for me to actually imagine what I have not yet gone through. Only by something happening or by talking through a situation with my family, am I able to imagine alternative ways that a situation might turn out. For example, it had never occurred to me that the park gate would be locked so I never had a chance to come up with a solution for what I would do if this happened (Answer: I walked back the way I came).

Something else that is hard about suffering from the freeze response is that even once I am 'unfrozen', there is a lingering feeling of being very, very tense. It takes me a long time to go back to feeling 'normal' again. So for example, my friend who made the surprise visit to my house may well have gone away feeling happy that he had seen me, but I was left feeling tense for the next few hours. The salespeople who come to my door leave me feeling awful too.

Being on my own or at home

One of the reasons why I choose to be at home or on my own is because it makes me feel less anxious. The fewer stimuli I am exposed to, the fewer things there are to feel anxious about. For example, a walk in the park with my dog would be considered by many neurotypical people to be a "relaxing" activity. Although it is enjoyable, it is not relaxing. There are many factors about being in the park with my dog that make me feel anxious, many of which would not concern most neurotypical people, for example:

Factor	Reason for anxiety	How to manage this problem
My dog's behaviour	She is quite unpredictable and may disappear off at any time, may not come back, or may want to see other dogs (which means I often have to talk to other people)	Go out at quiet time of the day, keep her on the lead, improve recall training
Other people who I do not know trying to interact with me	Other people often comment "what a lovely dog!" or "that's a big dog!" which might mean I have to stop and talk about my dog or listen to them talk about their dog	Go out at quiet time of the day, say the words and sentences I have learned to politely end a conversation quickly
Noise	When walking to the park, the traffic (such as lorries and motorbikes) can be very loud and can hurt my ears	Wear earplugs or go out at a quiet time of the day
Temperature	Hot weather makes me feel very uncomfortable	Wear appropriate clothing or go out early in the morning

Factor	Reason for anxiety	How to manage this problem
Meeting other people who I know	I have to meet the expectations of others because they are expecting me to present myself in the way they expect, or for me to be friendly and sociable. My routine can be disrupted if they want to talk for too long	Go out at quiet time of the day, take a less popular route, and learn how to politely tell people that I do not have time to stop and chat but that I would "love to catch up soon" or to "please text me"

These are some of the main anxieties I have merely from walking my dog in the park. Although some of the factors can be managed, some are out of my control.

At least when I am at home, I can control a lot of factors that would cause me anxiety if I was outside. For example, I can close the windows, doors and blinds to keep the noise level down and make the room a little less bright, I can put a fan on to help me feel cooler or just to provide a pleasant white noise silence, I can wear comfortable but only-house-appropriate clothes (such as pyjamas or old clothes that are full of holes, etc.). I do not have to look 'presentable', I do not have to talk to anyone, or answer the door or phone, my dog is safely inside and I can stick to my own timetable as no one can interrupt me… etc.

I live a life in which I tend to **minimise the chance that I will see people.** Social interaction always makes me anxious, at least to a small extent, no matter who it is and whether or not we have planned to meet. **Structure and advance notice around social interaction definitely help** to reduce my anxiety but it never goes away completely. When I am on my own I do not have that socially anxious feeling. Anyone who has ever suffered from anxiety will know what a burden it is to feel that way and how relieving and freeing it is when it disappears. It should be easy therefore, to understand why I prefer to be alone and indoors, if only just to stop that anxious feeling.

"What a lovely dog" example

I was walking my dog. I was wearing headphones as I normally do. They are big headphones so that people can visibly see them and hopefully will not attempt to talk to me. I often do not even listen to anything. I just want the sight of the headphones to deter people from talking to me. It is not necessarily because I do not want to talk, it is just that talking is very hard and having a conversation unexpectedly is one my most anxiety provoking moments. I am also very distracted thinking about my agenda for the day and the environment that I am in so, if someone tries to talk to me when I have not expected any conversation, my focus will be on where I am and what I am doing, not on any unexpected conversation. It all adds another barrier to communication.

As I was walking along, somebody said to me out of the blue, "What a lovely dog! I would love a big dog!"

It startled me that somebody was talking. I had not expected to engage in conversation and I wondered why they had not seen the headphones I was wearing, or if they had, why they still thought that I could hear what they were trying to say? In fact, I had not heard properly what they had said: 1) because of my headphones and, 2) because I had not expected to have a conversation and I was therefore not 'engaged' and ready to communicate with anyone.

So as not to appear rude, I took off my headphones (which takes a few seconds and which I find annoying) and said, "Sorry?"

She repeated what she had said. I often need people to repeat things twice or three times because it takes me so long to understand what they are saying. Usually the first time they speak I am so startled by the fact that someone is talking to me that I cannot understand.

"Thank you," I replied. I turned my back and tried to walk away but this lady kept on talking. While this was going on, I had my headphones in one hand and my dog on the lead in the other.

Because I have such a problem with motor coordination and executive function this was all proving quite difficult for me to do, in addition to having a conversation. The person kept talking to me about my dog. I was using so much energy in coordinating my hands, managing my feelings of anxiety and trying to filter out the environment (the wind and traffic noises can make it hard for me to hear) that there was very little energy left to actually listen and understand what she was saying. I had to say "Sorry?" and ask her to repeat her words after every sentence she spoke. All the while I was trying to work out how to end the conversation so that I could carry on with my own day.

Having choice

I think that most young people do not really know themselves well
enough to know:

1) what anxiety *is*
2) what it is like to *feel* anxious
3) *what* makes them feel anxious.

I also wonder whether anxiety gets worse when people go through
puberty? Not only do hormones naturally affect people, but also young
children do not really have much awareness of other people, and it is not
until puberty that we really become aware that we might be different
from other people. I was always "shy" but I do not think I had such
debilitating anxiety about being around other people until I experienced
puberty or until I went to secondary school (they happened at the same
time).

When we are young, we do not have much control over our life. Our
parents are really the ones who make the choices that affect us. Whether
or not we do something is usually the decision of our parents, not us. At
least this was the case for me. There were lots of things I did not want
to do, such as going to school, taking part in P.E. lessons, having friends
over or going to someone else's house, visiting places with my family,
going to the shops, having baths, coming off the computer, eating meals
I did not want to eat, etc. but I had to do all these things anyway because
my parents made me!

I suffered an enormous amount of anxiety when I was younger and I now
realise that it was due to the overwhelming effect of participating in too
many activities in uncomfortable environments.

It is now helpful knowing that I have ASD because it makes my family
and me understand that lots of things are genuinely very difficult and
anxiety-provoking. An ASD diagnosis can help other people appreciate
just how difficult normal daily experiences can be. Before my diagnosis I
wonder if my parents did not fully appreciate the severity of my anxiety.
Even I didn't know what anxiety really was. I did not know that the
symptoms I had (fast heartbeat, sweating, feelings of dread, trembling,
butterflies) all the time were not felt by other people all the time as well.
I knew that I really, really *disliked* lots of things, but there were also times
when I thought that other people felt the same way too and just put up
with things, or that I was not trying hard enough and that I ought to be
able to cope, or that if I did try harder things would eventually be easier.

Getting older has made me understand myself better. Learning about ASD and developing The Curly Hair Project has given me so much insight into why certain things are difficult and anxiety-provoking. My anxiety is less now largely because **I no longer do the things that cause me what I would consider to be significant anxiety** or that would have significant negative consequences (such as exhaustion or low mood). I *choose* the situations that I participate in. **I politely decline most invitations; and if I do decide I am going to do something, I am very careful about how and when I participate.**

I understand now that a major reason why I was so anxious when I was younger was because education was a very, very anxiety-provoking experience.

Being self-employed enables me to choose the activities I do and where, when and how I do them. It means being able to choose what time I wake up, what jobs I do, what assignments I am going to do, who I need to collaborate with, where I am going to walk my dog, what time I am going to go to the bank, who am I going to talk to, when I am going to see my friends, or when I am going to see the GP, etc. If I do not feel up to doing something on a particular day, I just do not do it.

Working flexibly has given me all these choices (so it is definitely something I would recommend to others on the autistic spectrum – you do however have to be organised, self-motivated and good at setting priorities).

Living in the moment

Learning to live in the moment has really helped me to feel less anxious. I think about what I am doing in the present and I shut out any thought of the future and the past. I think primarily about the current task, a little more about the rest of my day, and sometimes a little about tomorrow but definitely no further ahead. People sometimes ask me what I am doing at the weekend or whether I am looking forward to a forthcoming event. Most of the time however, I am not able to answer. For a friend who wishes to see me and wishes to put a date in their diary, I tell them that they can do that but to please ask me nearer the time to confirm. I will not be thinking about that forthcoming meeting until way, way nearer to the time!

I used to spend so much time worrying about events that were going to happen tomorrow and next week that it was debilitating. For example, when I spent the week working with colleagues who were planning to go out on a Friday night, I would spend every day worrying and contemplating how to avoid going. Now I think I would tell my colleagues straight away that I will not be attending and then stop thinking further about it. Getting older, and receiving my diagnosis, has helped me feel more confident about the choices I make and people seem to take me more seriously if I tell them that the reason I will not be doing something is related to my ASD as opposed to being "tired" or that I "just don't feel like it".

(It is really sad that it has taken a diagnosis of ASD for people to accept me the way that I am… A large driving factor for being involved in The Curly Hair Project is to help people become more understanding and accepting of those who are different from themselves rather than trying to change them or persuade them to be more like them.)

So because I have: 1) managed to shift my attention and be more focused on being in the present and, 2) managed to minimise the number of things I do that make me anxious, my focus, in any given moment is now more like this:

My current focus at any given moment

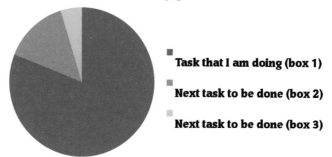

- Task that I am doing (box 1)
- Next task to be done (box 2)
- Next task to be done (box 3)

Example

When I am out walking my dog I am mostly thinking about her. I might also be thinking about my weightlifting which I will do when I get back, and I might also be thinking about some of the work I have to do today.

Previously, when I was thinking too far ahead into the future, I was not able to focus on what I was doing that day. In addition, because **I am now far more in control of my life, I do not have to do as many anxiety-provoking activities** and my focus is not wasted on being worried:

How my focus used to be at any given moment

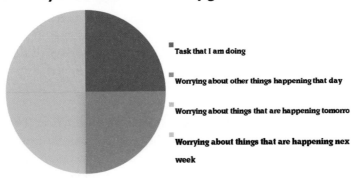

- Task that I am doing
- Worrying about other things happening that day
- Worrying about things that are happening tomorro
- Worrying about things that are happening nex week

Example

When I was out walking my dog, I might have been thinking a bit about her, but I might also be worrying about working, not having enough time for my workout, seeing my friend at the weekend, the Staff Night Out on Friday… etc.

Living in the moment therefore not only helps me cope with change, it also means I am a lot calmer and more productive each day.

Previously, my life was ruled by anxiety over past and future events. For example, when I was at school I would try as much as possible to listen to the teacher or to do the class work that I had been set but I felt so anxious about everything that had either happened or that was going to happen (such as the P.E. lesson that was next), that I could not really listen to the teacher at all.

If you look at the two pie charts above, you will see that the first one shows that 80% of my attention is being used on the task in hand, as opposed to in the second one where only 25% is being used on the task in hand. The other 75% is spent worrying!

Summary of how I have learned to live in the moment:

- I try to only think about today and the present task
- I aim to keep the number and type of anxiety-provoking events in my life to a minimum
- If I have to do a task that makes me anxious, I will make adjustments to lessen my anxiety so that I can better focus on the task rather than the anxiety

Mental energy

First I will say that, in this book, I have talked about three types of
energy: mental energy, physical energy and social energy. They
may all be slightly different but they also overlap. I have used them
interchangeably in my writing. Please use the terms in any way that you
find most helpful for you.

Let us say that mental energy is linked to executive function (I write in
more detail about executive function later but if you are not sure what it
means, executive function is the set of mental skills to help us do the basic,
normal tasks of life such as planning, prioritising, remembering, starting
and finishing tasks, etc.).

Let us say that mental energy can go up and down. The more mental
energy I have, the less anxious I am. Anxiety is very tiring so it makes
sense that a person who gets anxious also feels mentally tired and struggles
to do the normal tasks of life. When I am feeling anxious, I will probably
be far more likely to forget things, take a long time to do things, and
have difficulty starting and completing tasks. I am hugely productive and
competent when I feel relaxed. This in turn leads to having greater self-
confidence too.

There are some things that make me feel mentally energised and some
things that make me feel drained. You can probably already tell that the
following things make me feel energised:

When I am able to do these things consistently (i.e. over multiple days
and weeks) I feel more competent and less anxious. On the days when

these activities cannot be done or are disrupted I feel much more anxious, drained of energy and to be honest I do not perform well in my job and other activities.

By being able to **maintain energy-gaining tasks like these over a period of time** my mental energy increases and life becomes far less stressful. My brain just works better! Normal everyday activities become easier. I do lots of excellent work and I notice positive changes in myself, for example, I am more flexible, things that I would expect to make me anxious do not affect me as much, I am friendlier, more sociable and more communicative. I think that higher mental energy leads to higher social energy (the capacity to socialise). If a week has gone by in which my daily routine has not been disrupted and each box has been ticked every day, I would probably feel far more motivated to go and see my friends or feel that I could cope with doing something a bit different at the weekend… or even during a weekday! But if one or two days have been disrupted I would need time to recover from all the stress.

The periods in my life where I have really struggled to do and maintain activities that energise me (whatever they were at the time) have been my depressive periods. For example, when I was at school I just felt absolutely exhausted by the time I got home and didn't want to do anything. I would have tantrums if my parents wanted to take me out somewhere after school. I hated it when my friends wanted to come over to my house. However, I am sure if the school day had instead energised me I would have been far less reluctant.

If a person is exhausted then there needs to be enough time to allow the energy to increase. I never got enough time to recharge when I was at school. The days themselves were too exhausting. Even though my parents kept our evenings and weekends free most of the time, it felt as if there was just never enough time for my energy to increase enough to make a difference to my ability to function each day.

I think it is vitally important for an autistic person to decide which of their own activities and little 'rituals' are important for them, and to do these regularly, because these will give them their energy. I have found the four main things which energise me. As long as I get these done, I can be a bit more flexible in daily life and have enough energy to do other things too.

In the same way that I always decline an invitation to an activity that occurs at night because I need my time on my own to recharge, I also decline any invitation to activities that occur during the morning because my newspaper round, weightlifting and walking the dog routine is too important for my mental energy and ability to function. Sometimes people ask me why I cannot "just take a day off" weightlifting or why I can't "just do it at another time". I hope that if they care to read this book then they will now understand why I can't.

I need a high amount of mental energy so that I feel less anxious and so that I am more productive and competent in everyday life.

Constants

Using 'constants' is another helpful tool I have come up with that helps me feel less anxious. A constant is something that can be kept the same. Whenever I am doing something that makes me anxious or that is outside my usual routine, I try to maintain sameness in other parts of the day or situation. For example, when I go to an exhibition, the day in general will be different but there will still be some factors that I can keep the same, for example:

- I can bring my normal lunch
- I can eat lunch at my normal time
- I can go in my own car that I am familiar with
- I can do the newspaper round in the morning
- I can do weightlifting and/or walk the dog in the morning
- I can get home in time for my normal dinnertime
- I can have an evening that is the same

It is very important to remind and reassure myself that there are some aspects of the day that I can keep the same even if the day as a whole is going to be different.

> IT MIGHT BE HELPFUL FOR AUTISTIC PEOPLE TO FEEL IN CONTROL OF ANXIETY-PROVOKING SITUATIONS BY KEEPING SOME ASPECTS THE SAME. THIS IS A USEFUL STRATEGY TO REDUCE ANXIETY

Imagining situations

When faced with a new situation I like to know information about it in advance, such as who is going to be there, what we are going to be doing, where we will be, how long it will last, etc. This information means situations are *predictable.* It helps bring my anxiety down as things feel more in my control.

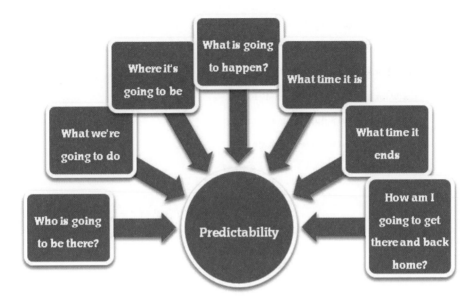

Having this information however, is not always enough to make me feel less anxious. I like to be able to imagine a situation too. **Being able to imagine how something is going to be helps** enormously in reducing my anxiety.

In order to fully imagine something that I have not done before I need to have the necessary information but I need to also become *familiar* with this information:

In order to make a situation feel familiar I like to:

1) experience small parts of it in advance
2) bring aspects of both me and my life as a whole to the situation.

For example, if I am going to go to a radio station to give a radio interview, the following will be helpful:

Information (predictability)

- Where do I need to go?
- What do I do when I arrive?
- What time is the recording?
- How long is the recording likely to last?
- Can I take breaks during the recording?
- Who is going to be interviewing me?
- What questions am I going to be asked?

Experiencing aspects of the radio interview in advance (familiarity)

- Listen to one of the presenter's previous shows
- Look up the presenter on the internet
- Ask to see a photo of the recording studio
- Have direct contact with the radio presenter by email in advance
- Ask to se photos of the building and car park

Bringing aspects of me and my life to the radio interview (familiarity)

- Bring my normal food and eat lunch at my normal time
- Make sure the interview takes place during Flexible Time
- Wear my favourite clothes
- Bring my own mug
- Commute in the way I am used to, e.g. car
- Do something that is familiar to me whilst I am there and waiting, e.g. visit my favourite website, listen to my favourite music, go to a chain coffee shop
- Bring my teddy bear (or even my dog!)

By making a situation both predictable and familiar, my anxiety can be reduced. Every situation always has a first time, but that first time can be made less anxiety-provoking if it can be made predictable and familiar.

Another important reason for making something familiar is that it can make me feel more confident. If I am familiar with the radio presenter and how the studio looks and can become familiar with my answers to the questions she or he is going to ask me, I will feel more confident.

Another example is that I have great difficulty learning something new and my motor coordination is not very good (all to do with executive function, to be discussed later). To help with this I always prefer to have or to use my own equipment. When I worked in an office I used to use my own laptop and even brought my own kettle! In P.E. lessons at school everyone would use the school tennis rackets but I would always bring my own. Having something familiar keeps my anxiety down because I know how to use it. It takes me so long to learn how to use something so at least if I use my own, it is one less thing to worry about (it also helps with my sensory and hygiene 'quirks').

When I did my personal training qualification we had to know how to use the gym weights machines, but because I do my exercise at home with free weights, I had not used machines before. All my classmates already knew how to use the equipment or they were able to work out how to use it very quickly. It took me such a long time in comparison. I used to have to visit the college gym outside of class time to practice on the machines. This was the strategy I used to make this situation more familiar (as I could not have that equipment at home).

This was not the only problem. The personal training exam took place in a different gym where all the weight machines were unfamiliar compared to those that I had used at the college gym during the course. Even though the machines were very similar to the college ones, this was, for me, another complete 'learn from scratch' task, so I went to that gym several hours before the exam was due to take place so that I could become familiar with the equipment.

Familiarising feelings

The brilliant part about getting older and understanding myself more is that I now know how a situation is likely to make me feel. For example, *I know* that when I go into a social situation that I am going to find it really, really hard and that it will probably make me feel very disconnected. I accept that this is how I am. It is good that I accept this because it means that I am more prepared for how some situations are going to make me feel. There are lots of situations that make me uncomfortable and **it helps being able to validate my feelings** so, before I go into a situation, I might say to myself something like, "This will be very hard for you" and "You are going to feel really left out, isolated or anxious" and "You might come away feeling really horrible".

(This may be somewhat contradictory and against a common therapeutic technique which suggests that if a person goes into a situation assuming it is going to be awful then it will be and if they think more positively then the situation will likely be more positive. This technique does not typically work for me.)

Assuming that a situation is going to be awful gives me far more comfort than going into a situation hoping and expecting that it will be an enjoyable experience or that I will make lots of friends, such as was my experience at that first Drama Club lesson. There have been many situations I have participated in naively thinking that I would have an amazing time "like everyone else". I now know that due to my ASD this is highly unlikely and a lot of the time, impossible.

So as well as making a situation familiar on a practical level, I like to get familiar on an emotional level too.

This is one of the reasons why **doing something that is difficult (rather than avoiding it) once or many times can be helpful.** The situation might not get less difficult but at least I will know what the discomfort is going to feel like and can get familiar with the feeling. **I like to know if something is going to make me feel negative, what sort of negative it will be and how long that feeling will last.**

The table overleaf gives some examples (not just related to anxiety – it can be used for any emotions). You can make your own table. I know that I may not have had the answer to how the activities would make me feel until they were actually experienced at least once. For example, I did not know that going to the Drama Club was going to make me feel awful. My hopes were set high and I thought I was going to find it fun and helpful.

Situation	How it makes me feel	How long does that feeling last
Going to a party	Isolated, overwhelmed	Several days
Going out with my work colleagues after work	Lonely, disconnected, anxious, isolated	Several days
Meeting up with an old friend who I no longer relate to	Lonely	Several days
Going to the dentist	Awkward and uncomfortable	The duration of the appointment
A telephone call	Awkward, anxious, confused	The duration of the call
Going to the cinema	Bored, agitated	The duration of the film

Be aware though that the first time is often the hardest – so for better accuracy, you may wish to try doing the activities more than once. Maybe if I had given it time those Drama lessons would have improved for me? But knowing myself now and knowing how other similar situations make me feel, I am glad that I gave it up straight away! I have been out with my work colleagues a lot of times and my feelings during those situations never change. Those situations still leave me feeling as awful as the first time, the only difference is that I *expect* to feel that way.

So I think 'repeated exposure' (doing something a repeated number of times which is a common treatment plan for people who suffer from anxiety generally) has other benefits even if the anxiety might not get any less. I have noticed that, even if I repeat some situations many times, the negative feeling is still just as strong. But it is still very helpful for me to **get comfortable with being uncomfortable and to know what feeling to expect.**

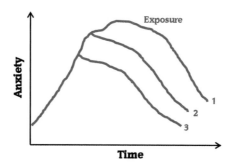

This is known as 'repeated exposure'. The graph shows that when a person participates in an anxiety-provoking situation the first time their anxiety is very high, but the more times they repeat the situation, the less their anxiety gets.

At least I predict nowadays that, if I go into a social situation, I know that I am going to feel X and I know what X is going to feel like and how long that X is likely to last. But perhaps I have only been able to know this because I have put myself in that situation many times?

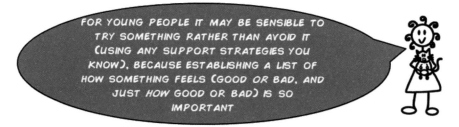

FOR YOUNG PEOPLE IT MAY BE SENSIBLE TO TRY SOMETHING RATHER THAN AVOID IT (USING ANY SUPPORT STRATEGIES YOU KNOW), BECAUSE ESTABLISHING A LIST OF HOW SOMETHING FEELS (GOOD OR BAD, AND JUST *HOW* GOOD OR BAD) IS SO IMPORTANT

My natural instinct was to avoid a lot of situations when I was younger but my parents made me participate anyway. I hated it (and them!) at the time but I do wonder now whether I am more resilient and know myself better because of it? I am someone who has done a lot of things at least once. All those experiences have helped me to have future experiences that are more predictable.

Sometimes it is the unknown of a situation that makes me most anxious. Not just the unknown of what, when, who, how, why, and where, but the unknown of "well, what is it going to make me *feel* like?" Sometimes the only way to answer that question is to do it and see.

Another strategy that helps me is to **remind myself that the negative feeling is not going to be permanent** and **I am always kind to myself after doing something that has been difficult** rather than being critical.

I say things to myself such as "You did really well to get through that" rather than "Why did you not do better?" (this was a particular thought I used to have, before I knew I had ASD).

Doing things immediately

A very common strategy to help autistic people feel less anxious is to plan things in advance. For example, planning to see your friend at the weekend or knowing that you are going to the dentist on Friday.

I always thought that I also needed to be able to plan everything in advance however, I now realise that for many things this is not necessary. There are at least four reasons for this:

1. Accepting that there will never be a right time:

I have accepted that, for me, if I do something that makes me even a little bit anxious (whatever that may be, such as seeing a friend, attending an appointment, going shopping…), there is probably never going to be a 'right time'. I just do not really like doing anything very much! If there is a choice between having a normal routine day, doing normal routine things versus doing something else (even if it is something I like), I always prefer to do the normal routine. The routine things are easy, convenient, predictable, efficient… and they do not cause overwhelming anxiety and tiredness.

2. Planning in advance gives a lot of time for thought and for the anxiety to build up and get worse:

The problem with planning is that it gives you a lot of time to think about why the plan was not such a good idea after all and allows time for the anxiety to build up. The lead up time often allows the feelings and thoughts of, "I wish I had not agreed to that" to appear. Often, this feeling is so strong that I will change my mind and cancel whatever it is, even if that is not the best outcome. It can result in feeling more isolated, letting down my friends and disappointing people, missing out on things that I am likely going to quite enjoy, or it can mean not doing things that are important (such as visiting the GP).

3. Never really knowing how I am going to feel:

I am not always sure how I am going to feel on the day (some days I can or want to do things, other days I cannot, which is usually dependent on how much energy I have available, how overwhelmed I am feeling, or whatever else has happened leading up to that day).

(I might have sporadic moments of feeling "socially energised" and when this feeling comes, I try to make the most of it by meeting up with people or doing activities immediately rather than planning them for a future time. Lots of people are not able to be so spontaneous, but I can at least try to see them and sometimes they will be free to meet.)

I will say however, that since having total control over my life, I am much more likely to be able to predict with certainty how I am going to feel on any given day so point number 3 is not as relevant to me now as it was in the past.

4. Plans create expectation and become a burden:

Planning in advance creates expectation and expectation puts pressure on me to be able to fulfil whatever is planned. Plans can therefore make me feel burdened. It feels like a weight on my shoulders that stops me from being able to fully focus on what I really want to be doing (my normal routine things). I do not want to feel restricted to, for example, being somewhere at a certain time.

On some occasions therefore **it is less anxiety-provoking for me to do things sooner rather than later.**

Seeing friends is an example. My relationships are very important to me so, even though it is really hard, I accept that I have to make the effort to see my friends. Seeing someone on the same day that I feel 'socially energised' means that there is less anxiety, less of a feeling of being burdened and less time to think about all the reasons why I do not want to socialise, as opposed to making a plan and spending all the time leading up to when I am supposed to meet my friend feeling anxious.

Often texting someone out of the blue and saying <Hello, would you like to walk the dogs in 20 minutes?> is far less anxiety-provoking and can be a realistically achievable way for me to socialise than to text <Hello, would you like to walk the dogs next weekend?>

Meeting a friend on Sunday example

Here is an example. A friend wants to meet up on Sunday. It is Tuesday today. I am unenthusiastic about agreeing to the meeting for all the reasons listed above, but I agree. By the time Sunday comes, I do not want to meet because I feel stressed and under pressure to fulfil the plan. If however, this friend had spontaneously texted me on Sunday saying <Hey, I'm in the area right now. Would you like to meet?> I would probably be far happier and more likely to say yes and go. It would still be a bit disruptive to my normal day but I would not have as much anxiety together with a feeling of being burdened, meaning that I am able to enjoy the socialising more.

Osteopath appointment example

Another example is when I visit my osteopath. The practice is busy so you have to make an appointment in advance. What usually happens is that I make an appointment and, when the appointment time arrives, I feel too anxious or I decide that right now is too disruptive or "inconvenient" and have to cancel the appointment. On the days when I feel like I want to make an unplanned visit to my osteopath, I can text them to see whether there is an appointment available, but most of the time there is not.

GP appointment example

Another example might be when I am feeling unwell and need to see the GP. When I try to make an appointment on the phone, they often say that I cannot have one until the following week. When this happens, I get really fumbled and cannot decide whether or not to agree to the appointment. However, if the receptionist tells me that they have got an appointment free "in an hour's time" and can I make it (maybe they say something like "actually, we've just had a cancellation and we could fit you in today?"), I would say yes. Perhaps one reason for this willingness and ability to go is that I am coping with the anxiety already by psyching myself up for the appointment and having made the telephone call, I do not want the anxiety to last, so at least if I go right now, the anxiety will soon be over. I am anticipating a disruption to my routine because of this appointment at some time or another anyway, so it might as well be now.

I also feel that by organising myself to make the call to book the appointment I have ticked 'half the box' already and now just want to 'tick the entire box'.

As you know, I do not like to leave things unfinished and to me having anything impending in the diary is a reminder that things are outstanding…

So often **I will try to do things immediately,** if I can.

As I write and am thinking about it now more carefully, I might even go as far as saying there is a good chance that often I will *prefer* to do things immediately.

The problem with being like this is that most activities can't be done so soon! For example, most people and my friends have busy lives and need to arrange things ahead of time; most services will only see people via an appointment. Things like going shopping, going for a walk, or to the bank are fine as I can go spontaneously and at practically any time.

Do not get me wrong, I will *never* "just go and do something" without knowing what is going to happen. I always need that information. However, I definitely do not always need lead up time. Perhaps predicting is more important than planning?

YOU MIGHT FIND IT LESS ANXIETY-PROVOKING TO DO THINGS NOW OR IMMINENTLY RATHER THAN WAITING FOR THEM. HAVING A LEAD UP TIME CAN MAKE THINGS WORSE THAN DOING SOMETHING IMMEDIATELY

PLANS ARE STILL VERY, VERY IMPORTANT, BUT THE PLANS DO NOT HAVE TO INCORPORATE A LONG DELAY BETWEEN THE TIME NOW AND THE TIME THAT THE SITUATION OR ACTIVITY IS GOING TO HAPPEN

Pinpointing triggers

Feeling anxious affects my overall experience and enjoyment of life. It means activities that should be enjoyable can be spoilt by the feeling of being anxious. For example, I quite enjoy going out for a meal occasionally, or going to the theatre, or even occasionally going to watch a weightlifting competition but, unlike neurotypical people, I cannot just feel "excited" and "happy" and "just go and do something".

Even if I am interested in doing something, the anxiety over factors such as: how will it disrupt my routine, what the environment is going to be like, how much socialising will I have to do, travel disruptions, etc. all severely reduce the likelihood that I will actually go through with my plan. It goes back to what I say when I say that I like the *idea* of things and often like to hear or read about things *afterwards* (I also like to hear people tell me about the interesting things they have done) more than actually experiencing them myself.

For me, if I really want to do something and not miss out, my strategy is to **pinpoint the aspects that are making me anxious** and come up with solutions for each aspect. This strategy requires a good level of self awareness because you have to be able to *recognise* what your 'triggers' are. For example, it is common for people with ASD (and even neurotypical children), to say that they "don't like" something, without breaking the situation down as to what it is specifically that they dislike. I was once told the story of a child who said he "hated Maths". But his parents and teacher eventually discovered that it was not Maths he hated, but where he was sitting in the classroom because the person next to him was too fidgety and annoying him.

If I wanted to go to the theatre, in order to minimise my anxiety, I would break down the situation into the various causes of anxiety and think about some things I could do to improve each part:

Disruption to normal routine	Plan in advance to have a non-routine day or a Write Off day. Make sure I have done everything I wanted to do (have ticked all my boxes) before going. Plan to be back home in time for normal dinner and bedtime routine
Travelling by public transport	Take a taxi or walk rather than the Tube
Lack of personal space inside the theatre	Book in advance a space at the edge of the row or by the door
The theatre being too hot or too cold	Enquire about the temperature in advance and dress appropriately
The play being too loud	Wear earplugs

The play overrunning or starting late	Expect for this to happen. Think about it in terms of a guideline time rather than a specific time (e.g. "It is going to start somewhere between 2.30pm and 2.45pm even though the start time states 2.30pm"). Remind oneself that even if it starts late, plays normally always end on time. But agree to leave early or at the right time if needs be

I am learning that **there are many things that I can do myself in order to make situations more manageable** and it means that I do not miss out on opportunities.

Structured and planned situations

I feel very anxious doing anything that is unstructured. For example, although I work mainly from home, my manager occasionally wants to see me at work. This can be made less anxiety-provoking if there is a **clear agenda** for the meeting (bullet points via email are brilliant). Although this situation is structured, i.e. I know that it will be just me and him in a room and building that I am familiar with, working through the agenda point by point, and although I know it will start and end at a certain time, there are still some aspects that make me feel the situation is unstructured:

Even if I have just gone in to have a meeting with my manager, I am still unsure whether I should interact with the other people that are also in the workplace, if only just to say hello and to ask how they are. But then, in order to do that, I first have to work out how to catch their eye. For example, it is really hard to know how and when to say "Hello, how are you? It's good to see you" when my colleague who is a receptionist is working on the computer, talking to a customer, or talking on the phone. I have to monitor the situation closely for an appropriate moment so that I can say what I want to say. If I do not ask how someone is, or say that it is good to see them, I worry that I will be considered impolite or unfriendly. Would I have done something wrong if I did not say anything at all? I do not know. What if the reason I did not say anything was because I could not work out the appropriate moment to speak and how to get the person's attention?

I also have the same problem working out how to leave. When I come out of the meeting with my manager I have to work out whether it is appropriate to say goodbye to the rest of my colleagues. I find this a confusing and stressful situation. I cannot work out whether I ought to because I came into work just to see my manager, nobody else, and everybody else is busy doing their own jobs. Since I work from home most of the time, I do not have a strong relationship with the other workers there, but I worry that, if I do not say goodbye, I will be considered rude or unfriendly. However, if someone is busy or if I am not able to time myself correctly and cannot catch their eye, or if when I speak my voice is too soft or not in the right tone, no one will have noticed anyway that I was there and that I left. This is a general problem I have when with people – because I have such difficulty with social communication. Even though I am trying really, really hard, I often do not communicate with them in the 'right' way. It is hard for me to navigate even the most simplest of social interactions, let alone develop relationships.

Difficulties around social communication such as working out whether and how to say "hello", "goodbye", and make small talk are most prevalent in unstructured situations or situations that involve lots of people. I am far more adept when it is **me and one other person only and in a situation that we had planned to be in.** This is why I can say hello and come across as friendly and chatty and have a successful meeting with my manager that we have planned, but struggle to know what to say in situations that are not like this.

A meeting scheduled with my manager eliminates some anxieties because he is expecting me, we have planned to say hello and to have a meeting, we have got an agenda already, but the small amount of time directly before and after the meeting that does not have a clear plan, is terribly anxiety-provoking. Unstructured moments cause many autistic people anxiety. Registration, the time before school or between lessons, were some of the most difficult times of the day for me as it was hard to know what to do and what to say. What is worse is that everyone else seems to automatically know what to do and what to say to each other. In fact, *unstructured* times are often the most *fun* for many neurotypical people (for example, children generally prefer times outside of lessons than in them!).

I have not yet worked out how to deal with the-time-just-after-the-activity-finishes, but there are two strategies I have learned to deal with the-time-just-before-the-activity happens:

- Occupy myself – read a book, listen to music, look on my phone
- Get there with very minimal time to spare – for example, if a meeting with my manager is scheduled for 11am, I will be nearby at 10.45am, but I will not actually go into the workplace until as late as 10.59am

- When I arrive early I go for a walk, because physical activity helps to calm me

Exercise, nutrition and sleep

There are a lot of treatment options for anxiety and depression but the best ones are simply meeting the fundamental needs of being a human being. **Take your exercise and nutrition seriously** and you will feel a lot better.

I believe that one of the reasons I love to be active is because, when I am anxious, my natural way of coping is to move or fidget. Being active makes me feel much better. I am the sort of person who will always **choose to stand** on a train rather than sit. I always get frustrated when a Receptionist tells me to "please take a seat" whilst I am waiting for an appointment, or when they assume that something is wrong because I am standing up!

I get my 10,000 steps in every day (even if it means occasionally having to go out walking at 4am. I try to never miss a day no matter how busy or tired I am!). I cycle and walk everywhere. I use a standing desk at home. My newspaper round means I am out on my bike each day at 5am. I lift weights most days. In the evenings I do stretching and massage.

I am a very fussy eater and I make sure **I eat something from all the food groups every day** to achieve a balanced diet. I eat a lot of protein to maintain and build my strength. People sometimes make unfounded remarks that I must be unhealthy because I do not eat F.R.U.I.T.[3], but, to be technically correct, I do, because I eat a lot of peppers, olives, avocados and cucumbers. Regardless, I eat a lot of vegetables, and vegetables are arguably a lot healthier than F.R.U.I.T. because they contain less sugar!

Sleep is very important. I have a very **regular sleeping routine** and go to bed and wake up at the same time every single day. I would never have a lie-in. My routine is far too important to me! Because of my good health and fitness, I rarely feel physically tired.

Having good physical energy means my mental and social energy levels are higher.

---

3 I do not even like saying or writing the word

Summary of how I manage anxiety:

- Have planned interactions
- Think in advance about all alternative outcomes to a situation and how I will respond to them
- Live in the moment
- Being on my own and/or being at home
- Use Constants
- Make situations predictable and familiar
- Make feelings predictable and familiar
- Do things almost immediately
- Pinpointing the exact factors that cause anxiety
- Incorporate structure and know what to do when times are unstructured
- Eating healthily, sleeping well and being active

WHAT i HAVE LEARNED ABOUT SOCiALiSiNG AND RELATiONSHiPS

Small talk
Social Energy Theory
Managing social energy
Social communication and interaction
Friendships
Educating others

Two enormous problems I have had throughout my life are: 1) socialising, and 2) having relationships with people. They are different problems. *Socialising* is being able to interact with other people (from family members, to therapists, managers and co-workers, shop assistants and strangers). *Relationships* form when I see people on multiple occasions or on an ongoing basis. Being able to successfully socialise with people is what leads to relationships.

Life creates obstacles and, often, there are more obstacles for a person who is autistic and therefore more difficulties to overcome in order to build and maintain relationships.

I have a small number of friends now, but for most of my life I have felt more or less friendless. The barrier formed by the glass jar[4] makes it very hard.

Other people don't seem to have quite as big - or encounter as frequently - obstacles as they go through life.

4 Rowe, A (2018). Asperger's Syndrome: Socialising & Social Energy. 2nd ed. London: Lonely Mind Books. 16–20.

*It is very hard to make friends
with a glass wall around you....*

*..that others do not seem
to have.*

I do not think I had any meaningful relationships outside of my family until I was about 21.

The transformation of 'socialising' into 'a relationship' is very hard; and once a relationship has been made it can be stressful if it is not carefully managed. I have therefore learned **the importance of building relationships with the right, and not the wrong, people.**

Socialising with people is… very, very hard. Because I have such difficulties with even the most basic of interactions, I am already at a disadvantage when it comes to attempting to form relationships with anyone at all.

When I see or spend time with people or even when I watch people on TV (even though I know it is not entirely realistic), they are mostly so socially adept. Most people seem to just socialise very naturally and plausibly; whereas I have difficulty in trying to work out the right time to say "hello", how and when I am even going to be able to get someone's attention, or how to work out if someone wants to talk to me, how my own body language ought to be, how to read someone else's… etc. I feel completely flustered whenever anyone starts to talk to me. Most people do not seem to experience the excruciating anxiety when they are spoken to that I experience.

"Is that the free newspaper?" example

I wake up, I do the newspaper round. Yesterday as I was on my bike a man called out at me:

"Is that the free Gazette?" (He pointed at my newspaper bag. He meant did I have the-free-Gazette-newspaper-that-anyone-can-have in my bag?)

I said no. He said "Oh OK" and got on with his day. I got on with mine but he had no idea that the conversation left anxiety lingering for several hours. I had not expected any interaction. I did not want any interaction.

When I am having a conversation with someone, I can often feel myself getting more and more exhausted and zoning out. My vision might even go blurry and I am no longer able to hear them speaking properly. Even if I am having an enjoyable conversation with someone my attention will not last, because I get too tired and then I feel distracted by my tiredness.

If I ask neurotypical people how they learned to socialise and make friends, their answer is usually: "I just knew!" It is done so subconsciously that they cannot even teach or explain how they do it.

Small talk

I have learned that **all relationships start with small talk,** but the problem I have with small talk is that it can be sudden, very dynamic and brief, and often there is very little time to think about a response, and a lot of it seems very 'autopilot'. Small talk often tends to happen unexpectedly (which leads to the aforementioned freeze response) or in an environment that is too busy or too noisy.

Simply put, small talk does not allow my true personality to show through. It also does not really allow my autism to show, which is actually very important to me, because if I really want to build a meaningful relationship with someone then I want that person to know I have ASD. I feel that most of my personality is hidden and not even noticeable by other people. They do not notice my general way of thinking, my skills and interests, which are unique, but also amazing and interesting. Most conversations in day to day life do not allow those things about me to come across. I am just a background person and listener or simply a very quiet person. If somebody wishes to get to know me, or see how I truly shine, it is not going to be through small talk.

However, **small talk is important.** The majority of the opportunities I have had, and the relationships I have made, have come because I made the difficult effort to have small talk with someone.

I have learned a few strategies to help me get the most out of small talk.

I have learned that **it is best to remain honest during small talk.** For example, if someone says to me, "What lovely weather today", instead of saying "Yes it is" (as I would have in the past), I will now comfortably respond "Actually it is way too hot/[other adjective] for me!". I do not want to say anything that is untrue because, should I wish to develop a relationship with this person, I want them to know the real me as much as possible from the start. I always have to be polite and friendly but in addition, I always try to be as honest as possible. **This is one way that I have reduced the need for masking.**

There have been times during small talk when I have been too honest and said too much when people ask me how I am. I have replied that I feel very anxious or that I would rather be at home or that the sound is too loud, that there is a smell in here that I do not like, that I am missing my routine… etc. but people do not really know what to say! The conversation either ends abruptly or they laugh and dismiss what I have said. I find it frustrating because I am not sure how people can expect to truly know and understand me if this is what happens. But I have learned that most people are not sure what to say if I am too honest and give too much detail too soon into our relationship. Instead, I have found a good balance that lets me stay true to myself – but that makes others feel comfortable – which is **being honest and polite but saying the bare minimum.**

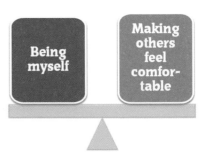

In small talk, I am honest but I am also brief and I say the minimum. It helps me start relationships off on the right track.

Saying the bare minimum also means I am less likely to say things I do not mean (because that is what happens when I do not have enough time to think quickly enough such as in fast paced small talk conversations). I therefore prefer not to say much because I would rather people thought I was very quiet rather than think I am someone I am not.

Social Energy Theory

Over the course of The Curly Hair Project, I have come up with an idea known as Social Energy Theory (© The Curly Hair Project 2018). A lot of people have told me that this idea changed their life and was the most valuable piece of information that they have taken away from my work. This is the theory that explained all the difficulties I have ever had with my social life and now **I use the Social Energy Theory to successfully manage my social life.**

Social Energy Theory states that all individuals, regardless of whether they are on the autistic spectrum or not, have different capacities for socialising.

The fundamental idea is that:

- Extroverts have more social energy than introverts
- Neurotypical people have more social energy than autistic people

There are lots of quizzes you can do to determine whether or not you are an introvert or an extrovert. **It is very helpful to know whether you are an introvert or an extrovert,** especially if you are at the extreme end of the scale like me:

Extroversion   **Introversion**

Social Energy Theory explains that:

- Extroverts gain energy when they socialise
- Introverts lose energy when they socialise
- Autistic people have a smaller capacity for socialising than neurotypicals
- Social energy can be measured as in a tank
- An individual needs to recharge when a tank is either full or empty (depending on if the individual is extroverted or introverted)
- **Everyone needs to be able to recharge** regardless of whether they are ASD and Introverted, ASD and Extroverted, Neurotypical and Introverted, Neurotypical and Extroverted, and the way that an individual likes to recharge is unique to them

(Personally I am not convinced that people can be *both* introverted and extroverted, but they can be more towards the centre of the scale; and an introvert can *appear* extroverted when their social energy is high, similarly an extrovert can appear introverted when their social energy is low.)

Social energy can be shown as being in tanks. When the tanks are at maximum capacities, they look like this:

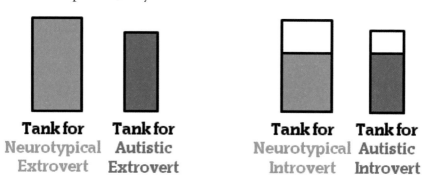

This table explains a bit more:

Person Type	What happens to their social energy level when they socialise?	How do they increase their social energy level?	When do they need recharge time?[5]
Neurotypical Extrovert	Increase	Socialising	When tank is full
Autistic Extrovert	Increase	Socialising	When tank is full
Neurotypical Introvert	Decrease	Time spent alone	When tank is empty
Autistic Introvert	Decrease	Time spent alone	When tank is empty

Introversion

I am very strongly introverted. This means that I need lots of Alone Time

5   This is a bit of an abstract concept. My idea is that even extroverts will eventually find they have had enough social interaction. I believe that this will happen once their social energy tank is full.

and that socialising makes me tired. My capacity for socialising is far less than the other three Person Types because I am also autistic.

I am learning a lot about being introverted in addition to having ASD. I am learning that although there are many neurotypical introverts, they do not have exactly the same difficulties as I do. They need their Alone Time, but they do not have a communication impairment, and this means that they can still integrate well with others. They also do not have all the other difficulties I have which include a strong need for routine, rigid thinking, impaired executive function and impaired sensory processing. Neurotypical introverts are likely to still have that common way of thinking and a wide range of interests. However, someone with ASD like me has a different way of thinking and very few, narrow interests.

When I observe people who I suspect are neurotypical and introverted, it is just another sign to me that I am different. For example, when I was at school, at university, or at work, I never saw anyone appearing to be craving Alone Time like I was, or looking as though they were desperate to escape like I was. Even when I talk to people who I suspect are neurotypical and introverted, they still appear to do a great deal more socialising than I do (I of course have some difficulties with being able to read people, but I am fairly certain that I have not yet come across anyone neurotypical who needs or wants as much time alone on a regular basis as I do).

Everyone I have known on a regular basis has always been more sociable than I am. They can go to school, they can go to work and do all the social interactions that come with these experiences, and yet they still appear to have some energy left to do other social activities afterwards. It is a bit surreal to me that there are so few people who need as much Alone Time as I do. It makes me feel isolated and reminds me that I am different.

(Disclaimer: Of course we can never truly know how someone else is. We can only go by what they tell us and how we see them behaving. There may well be lots of people who need as much Alone Time as I do, but because they are putting on an extroverted act, I just never see it.)

Throughout my life I always wondered why: 1) I felt so exhausted after spending time with people and 2) I did not seem to have as much motivation for spending time with people as everyone else did.

For example, why was it that at the end of a school day I was so desperate to get away from everyone and be on my own whereas everyone else seemed to want to go to the park together or go to each other's house for company?

Why was it that, whenever I went on an outing or dated someone, that the most time I could really manage was just an hour, whereas the other person would want to carry on and do more?

Online dating example

When I have been on an online dating website, the messages communicated prior to a meeting can be a bit like this:

Them: <What time shall we meet on Saturday?>
Me: <11am? But I will need to leave at 12pm>
Them: <Oh OK. Are you on a curfew or something?>
Or Them: <Why only an hour?>
Or Them: <We can't really do a lot in that time!>

And then during the date, as the hour is nearly up:

Them: "So what would you like to do now? Would you like to go and do [activity]?"
Me: "(Actually, it's time for me to go home now!)"

So one way that I, as an introvert, have learned to cope with socialising is to **have a time limit on social events** that I take part in. As you can see from the above conversation, people can, at first, find this request unusual. I have had to **learn ways to educate people** about why I am like this. It can be awkward, but the right person will not judge and will accept my wishes even if at first they do not quite understand. The way I generally describe it is that "because I'm autistic and quite a quiet person I get tired from socialising", or that "because I'm autistic I need to get back to my routine". This is another reason why my diagnosis has been useful to me. Of course I wish that I did not have to have a diagnosis in order to be accepted for being this way but sadly this is how it is in the world currently...

I did not really understand introversion when I was younger. **It would be good if introversion was taught in schools.** Even though my natural instincts have kept socialising to a minimum, I did not know there was a name for being like this. I always wanted to be home-schooled too. Other people however, seemed to be very pushy and would try to stop me from being so much of a loner. There were also many times when I thought that I ought to be a bit more sociable and to stop hiding away so much. Now I know that my natural inclinations were correct and that my need to be alone was actually a way of my gaining energy, keeping my stress levels down, stopping meltdowns, shutdowns and the general feeling of being overwhelmed and burnt out.

It can be very difficult to explain to people why I have such a great need to be alone (remember, for me it is a 'need', not just a 'want'), because most people, even neurotypical introverts, do not need as much Alone Time as I do. This need to have so much time alone makes me different. I think that some people take it personally because they think that I do not like them if I choose not to spend much time with them. Some people think that there is something wrong because I spend so much time alone. What they do not realise is that something will *go* wrong if I do not spend enough time alone.

I have learned to cope with socialising by ensuring that **I have enough Alone Time before and after socialising. I keep the number of social activities I have to a minimum and, when I do participate in them, I adapt them so that they do not exhaust me as much.** For example, if you remember in my last book, I talked about going on a Staff Night Out with my colleagues. They had planned to go to a restaurant and afterwards to take part in go-karting. My strategy to cope with this (and I really did not want to go to any of it, but I made a very big effort to be involved, as I knew it meant a lot to them that I was there) was to go only to the restaurant and then to go home whilst they went off to the go-karting circuit. You see, I was using this solution long before I was diagnosed.

When I now go out with my family I usually go on my bike so that I can leave when I want to. They go in the car. For example, at Christmas, if we go to my gran's house at 1pm, and my family all want to stay there until 6pm, if I feel tired I can leave earlier and go home on my bike. Everyone understands.

This strategy is one that I use which enables me to feel included and to participate in activities that I would otherwise have to avoid or say no to (even if I wanted to do them). It is a 'reasonable adjustment' that I make for me.

Having this lack of social energy is a very disabling and isolating part of being autistic. Life is so sociable all the time that if you are not that way inclined, it makes life very, very hard.

People always have expectations of one another whether intentionally or unintentionally. For example, people *expect* others to smile and say "Good morning". People I know *expect* me to stop and have a quick chat with them whilst passing in the street, just to be friendly and polite, even if just to say, "I can't stop, I'm in a rush!" All these things however are so difficult for an autistic person like me. A lot of the time I cannot, or do not want, to have to meet those expectations.

"Say good morning then!" example

I went in to the shop to collect my newspaper round. There were already a lot of customers at the front of the shop in a queue. The crowd made me very anxious. I noticed there was someone I saw regularly in the queue so I tried really hard to be polite by smiling at her as I made my way through the queue to the back of the shop to get my newspapers. I had my headphones plugged in. As I made my way to the back of the shop, there was a tap on the back of my shoulder, which made me freeze with anxiety. I turned around and the customer said loudly, "Say good morning then!" Everyone looked at me. It made me feel awful. Then I had all this lingering anxiety for the rest of the morning.

I tend to **go out during quiet periods of the day** to avoid the likelihood of seeing people and **I wear big headphones** even if I am not listening to anything. **I wear a baseball cap or have my hood up** so that people are less able to notice me. Sometimes **I pretend to be doing something** on my phone hoping it gives me an excuse as to why I am not talking or noticing someone should they see me.

Perhaps a reason I struggled to make friends within certain settings (such as at school, university, work) was because I needed more Alone Time than other people needed. Spending a lot of time alone means there are less opportunities to build relationships. An additional unfortunate consequence of being alone so much is that, whilst I am alone, my friends are with each other making their own relationships even stronger. It can lead to feeling very left out. An example of this is when I did my placement year at university. Another student and I joined a team at the laboratory. I spent all my breaks on my own, whereas she spent her breaks with other team members. Within a week she had made lots of friends, and I still knew no one.

Managing social energy

Living in a majority neurotypical world means that most activities are set up with neurotypical people in mind. Having ASD means these activities do not allow for enough Alone Time and time to recharge. For example, most neurotypical people have no major difficulty going to school or work for 6-8 hours a day, plus time for commuting, 5 days a week. They still manage to have a life outside of those hours, seeing friends, doing errands, as well as incorporating enough recharge time when needed.

I actually once received an email from my colleague. The email said:

<Dear all,
As you can see, we've been struggling to have regular team meetings because our jobs are so busy! We have therefore decided that these will now have to take place after work. We really hope you will attend. Pizza will be provided!>

I saw one reply from another colleague that said, <That's fine. I'm happy to do this>

The only thought that went through my head was, how will I manage to get enough of my critical time to recharge if I am expected to attend these meetings too? (Luckily I do not have to!)

Don't get me wrong, I have no doubt that some of the people are unhappy about this, but it is probably for different reasons than mine. They are probably unhappy about it because it consumes 'family and social time' rather than 'Alone Time' (or just because they dislike their job!). This is another difference between me and other people. My priorities and my needs seem to be different. Even if the business was paying people to attend those meetings, I would not go.

For an autistic person I suggest that traditional working or educational set-ups do not allow for enough time to recharge. This is relevant to both introverts and extroverts. An autistic introvert will find their social energy drops each day, not leaving enough time for it to go up again. An autistic extrovert will find their social energy goes up each day, but reaches its limit too frequently (remember, my idea is that an autistic extrovert needs time to recharge when their tank is full rather than empty). Reaching maximum social energy capacity too frequently may cause them to feel overwhelmed.

The social energy consumption each day, assuming:

1) an autistic introverted person like me starts off with a smaller level of social energy (remember that our tanks are smaller)
2) a lack of time alone each day, means the graph would look like this:

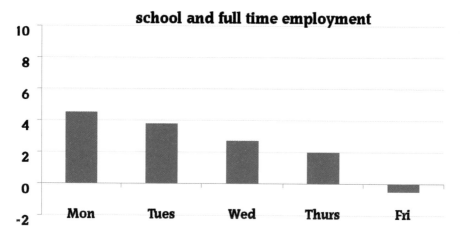

Graph showing decreasing social energy during school and full time employment

When you look at this graph, you can see why an autistic person might need to spend their weekends and evenings on their own. They need that time to recharge. Or you might understand why an autistic person may feel they have "no life" outside of work, as exhaustion means that, even at the weekend and during evenings, they are not able to do the activities that they enjoy because that time is spent pretty much doing nothing and recharging instead (similar to how I have to spend my evenings).

Going to college and university were a bit less energy-draining as the days were shorter and there were more free periods in which I could be alone. Not only were college and university less socially intense (which meant my social energy was not exhausted so quickly anyway), I had more Alone Time throughout the week during college and university than I had at school. The social energy graph was probably more like this assuming had a free day on a Wednesday for example:

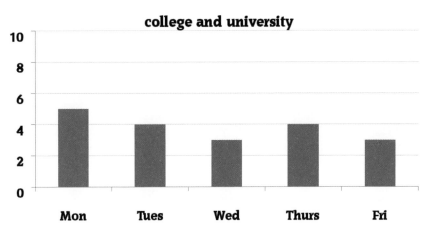

Graph showing social energy levels during college and university

Being self-employed has been the best thing for me because I do not have to participate in many social energy-draining activities and there is a lot more Alone Time to recharge every day. So now my social energy chart looks a bit more like this:

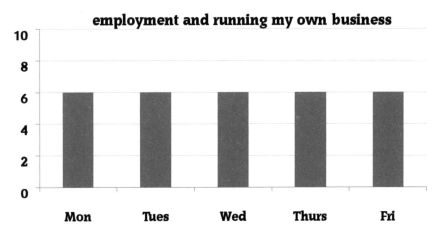

Graph showing social energy levels during self-employment and running my own business

Notice how not only is my social energy quite high every day (in fact, 6 is probably always the maximum for me, my tank is never full), it is *consistently* high, which helps a lot with my mood.

When I compare these three graphs, I think it explains why I had so many mood swings when I was younger. It was because exhaustion made my energy level wildly fluctuate. Having fluctuating energy is exhausting in itself!

My life is solitary in comparison with most other people, but solitude allows me to function well and improves my mental health. People always comment both now and in the past that they "never see me". I do not socialise much both through choice and through necessity. I have very brief, regular interactions when I go to the shop to collect my newspaper round and when I go shopping and sometimes when I walk my dog I have to make small talk with people. But that is generally it.

One of the things I most commonly hear from autistic people is how they feel "tired all the time", and therefore cannot keep up with their education or work, or they have periods of complete burnout. I am one of these people too. It is because life for autistic people seems to be more energy-draining than for neurotypical people. Therefore, more time for recharging is needed, which, in reality, is very hard to achieve.

Education and being in employment consumed almost all of my social energy which left very little for other relationships. This also explains why I am more inclined to see my friends now that I work from home on my own.

I have learned that there are three factors that affect how likely I am to go and see my friends:

I have learned that social energy is the most important factor.

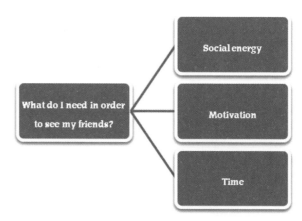

So my capacity for socialising is less about having more time available, it is about having more social energy available. At least working from home on my own every day gives me more social energy to spend time with my friends *if I want to.* I still lack the motivation to see people, but at least I do not feel so exhausted that I *cannot* see them. If I have enough social energy I can usually cope with seeing people even if I do not really have time and even if the motivation is not really there. If I do not have social energy I really struggle seeing people because I feel so tired.

Motivation is harder to change and usually comes if I have a purpose for seeing someone as opposed to seeing them for the 'sake' of it (i.e.

'socialising'). Motivation is usually only there if it is the 'right' person and the 'right' situation. I think introverts would always find they lack motivation in comparison to extroverts.

I am good at prioritising and organising myself so making *time* to see my friends is never a problem for me.

In conclusion, it has been very hard for me to have relationships with people throughout my life just because I was never having enough time alone. Now that I have more **regular and consistent Alone Time,** I have much more energy to see people and to develop my relationships. Socialising is still exhausting, but perhaps not as much as it used to be. It is because my normal initial level of energy is higher now so I have more: 1) social energy to begin with and 2) more social energy leftover.

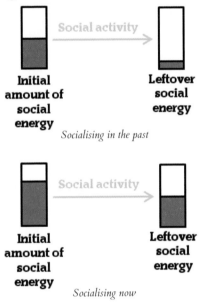

Initial amount of social energy

Leftover social energy

Socialising in the past

Initial amount of social energy

Leftover social energy

Socialising now

Social communication and interaction

Spending lots of time alone increases my social energy, but there are other reasons as well:

Socialising with other people exposes my social difficulties. Autism is defined in diagnostic criteria as the individual having persistent difficulties with:

1) social communication
2) social interaction.

The *social communication* impairment means, for example, I am not sure what to say to people, I am not sure when to speak, how to reply, and that I struggle with eye contact. I struggle to listen and understand verbal language and I take language very literally.

The *social interaction* impairment means that I cannot normally relate to people's hobbies and their day to day experiences of life. I accept that I 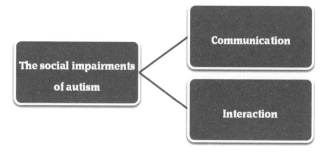 am different but a lot of the time I do not want to *feel* different, because *feeling* different is usually isolating. It is nice for me to feel that I am less different because then I do not feel as though there is as much 'wrong' with me. This hugely increases my self-esteem.

At least if I am alone my social difficulties do not affect me.

Socialising can make me feel very lonely. Being alone is not the same as being lonely (a lot of people confuse being alone with feeling lonely). I choose to be alone so that I can recharge, think, do my hobbies and projects. I do not *choose* to be lonely, which is feeling disconnected, not relating to others, being left out, ignored, disliked and rejected.

To articulate to other people how lonely I can feel can be difficult because other people often think that my loneliness is self-induced. It makes logical sense that if a person declines a social invitation and subsequently spends so much time alone, even when there are opportunities to be with other people, then it will cause them to feel lonely. I remember once having a conversation with my therapist. I told her that I felt lonely. She asked me what I did at the weekend. I told her that a friend had invited me out but that I had declined. Had my therapist been someone who did not understand, rather than the very helpful therapist she was, they would think this loneliness was self-induced.

One reason I often decline social invitations is because I have learned that pushing myself to socialise, when still not fully recharged, makes the socialising stressful and overwhelming, which then leads to feeling disconnected from people, which then leads to loneliness. Having enough Alone Time enables me to have enough social energy to get through the next social situation and be able to enjoy my time. Having Alone Time also enables me to build up that motivation and desire to actually go and see people and, because I am re-energised, I enjoy the time I spend with them and come away feeling more connected.

Socialising with the 'wrong' person or in a group can also make me feel very lonely, so I would rather avoid those situations. I feel that there is a lot of pressure in any sort of group situation to either fit in or to appear to be better than everyone else. There is a lot of peer pressure. One example I remember is from my placement year at university. My manager used to push me to go and spend time with the rest of my team during breaks and lunch times. She was trying to make me fit in. In most of the jobs that I have had, there has been pressure and expectation to be a team player. But I just do not fit into situations as easily as everyone else does. When I try to I just feel awfully lonely because it is so hard. I am just not as sociable and not as adaptive as other people. Put me in any social or public situation and you can be sure that it will be me who struggles the most, me who gets left out, me who cannot work out what I am supposed to be doing. I am the one who is most different. **I have learned to be very selective about the group situations I put myself in,** otherwise I avoid them.

Talking and listening

Most people talk to each other in order to feel connected. **I however have to be careful because talking to people can make me feel very disconnected.** I typically do not like talking with people because a lot of people seem to have common interests that I do not share (things such as 'going out', holidays, sports, travel, family, films, fashion, celebrities) or they might have an interest in common with me (albeit rarely) but they view it differently. Sometimes, when I tell someone about something I have done that might include one of those normal-type of interests, for example 'going out', I receive interested, passionate feedback as opposed to if I tell them about my weightlifting or what I am working on (the things that I find genuinely interesting and are important to me). I can tell that they are not as engaged and they sometimes look bored. I can tell this is not just because of their body language and facial expressions but also because the conversation we are having is brief, non-specific with just a few - if any - questions.

It can be isolating and difficult to talk to people about my life and my interests because I am unusual.

So **I try to connect with people on their level by listening to them** rather than talking about me. The reason I might choose to talk about the aforementioned common, 'normal'-type interests is because it is what in general I feel people like to discuss. I think the phrase that "people feel comfortable with what they know and nervous about what they don't" is appropriate. If I talk about 'normal' things, 'normal' people know what to say and are able to relate. If I talk about 'uncommon' things 'normal' people are not sure what to say because they are unable to relate. As previously mentioned, the times when I have tried to talk to people about some of the less common interests I have, such as my weightlifting, or specific aspects of my work, I receive a rather superficial or blank reaction. But if I talk about going to the cinema or visiting my family people are much more interested and more willing to respond.

Generally, I have learned that **I much prefer to listen to someone talk about what they are interested in than for me to talk about something that is not one of my rigid or narrow interests.** I find it hard to talk about things that I am not really interested in or, worse, that cause me stress. For example, just because I went out yesterday evening, went on holiday last month or saw my sister last weekend, does not guarantee I will want to talk about those things even if other people want to hear about them.

I am, however, happy to hear about other people's lives, even if I cannot relate, as it does not always make me feel isolated. It can be interesting and develops my understanding of other people. You will find me often saying to my friends outright, "I don't want to talk today so you can do all the talking".

However, I have learned that I tend not to have much to say about the subjects that I cannot relate to. I also find it easy to lose track of conversation that is about subjects I not familiar with. I am happy to listen, but the listening will require more focus. I tend to process language word by word and line by line. If the conversation is about something I know about and can relate to, even if I lose focus for a moment, I can get back on track quickly or fill in what I missed using logic, knowledge and intuition. If it is about something unfamiliar, then every word and line matters.

Perhaps another reason why I felt so isolated at school and university is because I could not really relate to the subjects people talked about despite trying to maintain focus. I tended to just zone out. Even at a family gathering I can lose track of what is being discussed not necessarily because I am disinterested, but because I have not been able to maintain enough focus due to the effort involved in paying attention. There is also far more effort involved in working out how I feel about what they have said and how I should respond. If I have never been in that particular situation, and cannot relate to it at all, it is incredibly hard to decide how I feel about it. I really struggle with having empathy.

I need people to be excellent at getting to the point and being able to summarise!

I said before that any reminder that I am different *usually* gives me a feeling of isolation. *Sometimes* it does not. **Having a conversation with someone I care about who is different from me can make me feel connected.** It can most certainly be interesting, rather than isolating, to hear about another person's life. Often it depends on who they are and the way they are talking. It is not really the way someone lives or the things they do that make me feel different, it is the way they think and the way they respond to me.

If somebody I genuinely care about, who might have quite a different life experience to me, engages in conversation I will enjoy hearing about it. Maybe they are very extroverted and the most 'normal' sort of neurotypical person possible! But it does not matter. If they understand me and know how to communicate with me it does not matter how different we are. I will still feel connected to them, not isolated.

Someone I used to be able to relate to but can no longer (because they have changed) will be difficult to converse with. Someone who comes across as quite narrow-minded and is not accepting of difference will make me feel isolated.

Although I am largely a listener, **I can be talkative if someone is interested in the activities that I do** or my work at a deeper level. When a person takes a genuine interest in me and asks interesting questions, I will be very talkative with them.

However, sometimes I still prefer not to say much about the things I do because some people, if they are genuinely interested, can generate a response full of excitement and enthusiasm that brings about too many ideas and possibilities and makes me feel overwhelmed. It takes me a lot of time and a lot of hard work to commit to the things I do and to have achieved what I have achieved, but I need to do it all in my own way. If someone else gives too *much* feedback, or too *many* ideas, it can put me off talking to them entirely! For example, I told someone that I was making an animated film and their immediate reaction was "That is so cool! What are you going to do with it?" and "You could do [this] or [that]!" and "Oh and definitely make sure you do [this]!" I found it overwhelming!

I do not mind people having ideas but usually I prefer them to brainstorm ideas about *their own* projects not mine! Too many ideas from other people about my own projects can make me feel stressed! Also, as you know, I like to live in the moment. If I am making an animated film then that is exactly what I am doing. I am not yet thinking about what I am going to do with it when it is finished.

I am therefore **very selective about the people I converse with.** The 'wrong' people will leave me feeling very isolated and the 'right' ones will make me feel connected.

Understanding and empathy

Another reason I prefer to be alone is that lots of people do not want to, or cannot understand me; I would rather be on my own than spend time with someone who does not make any effort at all to understand me. I am always making an enormous effort to understand other people.

There is no point spending time with someone who not only is different to me, but who chooses to judge, ridicule or change me, or does things that are inconsiderate rather than learn from me and try to have an understanding. For example, I do not want to spend time with someone who might tell me that I "should have had a big party!" on my birthday instead of spending my birthday on my own at home. I do not want to spend time with someone who tries to persuade me into going to a film festival where my film is being shown, when I have already explained to them that I am probably not going to attend due to my ASD difficulties. I do not want to hear them say the words "it'll be fun and you'll miss out!"

I understand that lots of people are not intentionally trying to upset or annoy me when they say these sorts of things. Their reactions are very 'normal' reactions, but such comments can make me feel very misunderstood - and often very upset - because they remind me of how different I am, and therefore I feel isolated. People say these things because that is how *they* see the world and that is how *they* experience life. A lot of people would enjoy having a birthday celebration or feel proud to attend a film festival where their film was being shown. I do not enjoy such activities.

I still have difficulty with people understanding the true extent of my difficulties. For example, someone I know, although extremely nice, asks me questions on the spot or talks quite quickly and changes subject quickly. She is someone who will knock on my door unexpectedly. This is an example of someone who I would rather avoid.

During periods when I am very quiet, I still sometimes get people asking me "What's wrong?" and "Are you OK?" I know that they mean well but really they need to leave me alone. Responding to such questions just takes even more energy and can lead to further conversations that I do not want to have. For example, saying "Yes, I am OK. I just need some space" leads to "Oh OK. Why, has something happened?".

This can sometimes be an example of someone who struggles to put themselves in my shoes, as their questioning is related to how *they* would like someone to treat them if *they* were tired or stressed, not how I like to be treated. It is also another example of how difficult (impossible?) it can be for someone who does not have autism to imagine how it must be to feel that fatigued and overwhelmed from socialising in daily life where, not only do you want to be left alone, but you also physically struggle to talk or to write. To expect or hope that someone who has autism will be able to explain what's wrong or why they need space when they are already in that 'shutdown' stage is a lot to ask for. I have lost a lot of relationships because people were not able to understand my need for time and space.

One of the reasons that I have dissociated myself from many of the people I used to know is because it can be difficult to remain in touch with some of the people who knew me before my ASD diagnosis. I feel a bit uncomfortable being around them because the person they saw and the person I presented was doing a lot of masking and was very unsure of herself.

I might be able to carry on having a relationship with them, but only if I could get over my awkwardness and if they were truly willing to understand. Some people are just unable to, for whatever reason.

It is hard, upsetting, and a bit embarrassing to explain to the people who knew me in my 'masking' days, why I was able to do things at that time (such as socialising, participating in other people's activities, travelling, certain jobs) and why I was able to be spontaneous and flexible, and why it seemed as though I was 'enjoying' doing those things at that time, yet now I do not really do any of those things because I do not and never did truly enjoy them. I only participated in them because I thought they were the things that I *ought* to be doing and it was how I was *supposed* to be. This was not helped by other people putting pressure on me to be more sociable and to participate, stating that there was something wrong with me if I chose to be on my own instead.

I still like the people I knew from the past and I care about them but it is difficult for me to be around them as the person that I now am. I want to be clear and remind the reader that it is not that I have changed nor that I was insincere. Writing this book has truly made me realise that I have always been the same person inside, I just got a bit lost bringing that person out and the world and the people around me were not very good at helping me along the way. How a person 'presents' at any given time is dependent on who they are presenting to and the environment they are in. I also believe that many people do not have much empathy (especially young people, which partly explains why peer pressure and bullying are so prevalent).

Some people who knew me before I had my diagnosis of ASD can feel confused and disappointed because I will not do the things I used to do. "But you used to like doing that" or "You never used to be such a hermit" are typical remarks made to me. My reply tends to be that I did not really enjoy doing those things (but either hoped that I would if I tried hard enough, or thought I *should* like doing those things) or that I might not have always *been* such a hermit but I always *wanted* to be one. I now understand my needs far more. I understand that doing too many activities that make me stressed causes me to shut down. Living a much more restricted life means that I do not have as many shutdowns and I am able to function more consistently.

This is the reason I am more restrictive now about what and when I do something. I just do not want to live a life of being in a state of shutdown and not being able to function, especially doing things that I am not really interested in anyway.

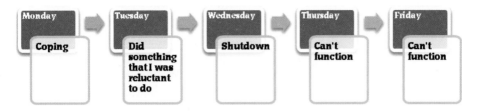

Monday		Tuesday		Wednesday		Thursday		Friday
Coping		Did something that I was reluctant to do		Shutdown		Can't function		Can't function

I used to do a lot of things that were too much for me, just because I thought that is what I ought to be doing or that was how other people wanted me to be. But it led to an incredibly stressful life.

Masking

I describe masking as 'the degree to which an autistic person appears neurotypical'. Lots of autistic people mask, especially females. I completely understand why people mask and it often happens subconsciously. However I have learned that whenever possible it is a lot better not to. The most significant problem masking causes is that it makes relationships insincere and untruthful.

One of the major benefits of minimising the amount of masking is that I have built genuine relationships with people. I realise that **I am most lonely when I am around people and when I am masking at the same time.** When I am masking, people are not seeing the real me, because I am not being the real me, so how can I expect to have a meaningful relationship with them? It is not possible.

It is only now that **I understand my difficulties and can explain them to others** who are willing to listen and take the time to understand, that I have been able to develop meaningful relationships.

I am able to mask a lot less now because:

I understand that my difficulties and the way that I think are all genuine and that there are lots of other people in the world like me. This is just the way I am wired. I have greater appreciation of my strengths and uniqueness and can see the positives in being the way I am. Without my diagnosis, I was not fully able to appreciate myself as I was focusing too much on what was 'wrong' with me and questioning why I was so different as opposed to knowing and accepting who I am.

I think life is far better for people on the autistic spectrum in 2018. Even in the small number of years since I was diagnosed, so many good things have happened in the world to improve the awareness and understanding of autism. I am always hearing that more and more people are getting diagnosed and that girls are getting diagnosed earlier. Schools are definitely doing far more to help autistic students. The general public are becoming more aware and understanding of autism. There have been several programmes on the major TV channels at prime time that have been produced sensitively and accurately about people with autism. I hope that people now do not feel they have to mask as much as I felt I had to. I believe people now are generally more open to different world experiences and tolerant of individual differences. I have no doubt that The Curly Hair Project has contributed to this. I am proud of my contribution to the world and the improvement in the understanding of autism.

I now have a lot more control over the situations I participate in and the people I spend my time with. I incorporate helpful strategies and avoid situations that make me overly anxious and this makes me less likely to feel I have to mask.

I care less about what other people might think of me. Being able to tell people that I have ASD has helped me feel comfortable by feeling less need to mask. If I do tell someone then they can *expect* me to be a bit 'different' which in turn means that they will not expect me to be a way that I cannot be. There is no point people expecting me not to be different – because I am – and then having 'normal' or 'neurotypical' expectations of me. I do not tell everyone I interact with that I am autistic but I do tell people when I feel or believe that we might have a future relationship, for example, because we are going to be working together or because I want us to become friends. By telling people I am giving them the opportunity to think about me a little differently. They are more likely to be more understanding of my habits such as the need for time alone, the strong chance of me saying "no" to meeting up, my direct and blunt nature… etc.

As to whether or not, when, and exactly how to tell people I have ASD? These questions would have been a worry if I was in a different situation to the situation that I am in, but I am indeed in a bit of an unusual position as I generally always have to mention my job when I meet people (one of the most common small talk questions is to ask someone what they do) and so I end up telling most people that I have ASD anyway even if it feels really awkward and unnecessary to do so! For example, if I get chatting to someone whilst walking the dog or even if I go into the bank to pay in a cheque (the cheque is made out to "The Curly Hair Project"), small talk often leads to the cashier asking me "The Curly Hair Project, what's that then?"

With people I know and in planned situations, I am definitely more able to be myself. Most importantly, I have been able to **achieve that very important balance between being myself and being able to come across as neurotypical** enough to navigate life comfortably and do the things that are important such as working and typical errands like going to the bank and going shopping... but still autistic enough that I am honest and open with people and have relationships.

I have noticed that small talk and spontaneous interaction are two scenarios that always cause me to mask. I have noticed that I am more likely to mask when: 1) I am anxious, and 2) the situation is unexpected (and 2 always causes 1). Unexpected social interaction makes me pretend to have social skills. The masking tends to happen as a result of feeling 'frozen' with anxiety. Using strategies to make situations less anxiety-provoking also means I do less masking.

Structure

During the last couple of years, my main socialising is when I walk my dog with friends. I can cope with this because it is **a structured activity** that is **quiet and peaceful** (a one to one walk in the park is far less stimulating than a noisy, crowded shopping centre, cinema, pub, or a party... or at school or at university).

I also occasionally meet my friends for a one hour cup of tea in a café or I might go to their home. Other strategies I use for socialising are to carefully choose the environment in which to socialise and confirm *ahead of time* how long the socialising is going to be. **Quieter environments and shorter durations of meetings are best** because they leave me less exhausted and less overwhelmed.

I have learned that the only way I can really ever enjoy socialising is through **very structured interaction or activity.** I always need to know:

- What we are going to be doing
- What time we are going to be meeting
- What time we are going to finish
- What the purpose of our meeting is

Purpose

Sometimes there is no purpose other than that the person likes seeing me and enjoys my company, or vice versa, and that is completely fine too *as long as I know that this is the purpose!* It makes me feel far more comfortable if someone says outright to me: "Hello Alis. I would really like to see you because I enjoy your company and for no other particular reason."

I do not think neurotypical people need such obvious explicit remarks said to them, but I do. I always want to know *why* somebody wants to see me or what they want to know and I want them to tell me quickly. A text or instant message from someone can make me feel nervous as I often do not know what they want quickly enough (people tend to take too long to get to the point and sometimes they do not have a point at all, which is fine, but I want to know that):

Them: <Hey, how are you?>
Me: ("What does he/she want? Do they want something? I feel anxious")
Me: <Hello. I'm fine thanks, you?>
Them: <Yep, good thanks>
Me: ("Do they just want to have chit chat or do they want something? I feel anxious")

Socialising using text or instant message can make me feel nervous because I am not sure what the person wants. If they want to have small talk I would like them to say that and, if they want to ask me something or they want me to do something, I want them to get to the point straight away. I am a bit unusual because, if someone wants something from me, I do not need them to be polite and ask me how I am beforehand or to make small talk with me. **I feel most comfortable when people get to the point straight away.** Those social courtesies are not needed with me (unless they genuinely would like to know how I am). If you want something from me, feel free to ask outright and straight away! I understand that a lot of neurotypical people feel a bit hurt if courtesies are ignored or if they are only ever contacted because someone else needs something but, with me, that is my preference! Be clear, be concise, and get to the point.

If someone just wants to do small talk with me I would like them to be blunt and say so:

Them: <No particular purpose to me messaging you. I'm just chit chatting>

I still do not particularly enjoy small talk but at least, once it is established that this is small talk, I feel a bit less anxious.

People who know me expect me to be pretty unresponsive. If my Mum texts me I will give her the reply she needs (for example, if she asks me how I am, I will reply, but that is the bare minimum and that is all I say). If she wants to know something she needs to be direct and ask. This is in comparison to my neurotypical sister who will have long text conversations with our Mum, even if there are no direct questions.

Small talk, or talking for the sake of talking, generally makes me very uncomfortable and tense and it is not something that comes naturally to me. Generally **I prefer only to interact with someone when I want to know something or when I want them to know something.**

I find that interacting with my *colleagues* is often the easiest form of interaction. The majority of socialising nowadays is with my colleagues and the interaction is always to do with getting something done.

Perhaps this is another reason why I find it hard to stay in touch with my friends and why I have little desire to see them. Interacting with my friends is not to do with work and 'getting things done', it is more about keeping up with each other's lives, which isn't specific or purposeful, so does not come easily to me. To talk to my friends because they are my friends and to keep up with what they are up to is lovely, but it is much more difficult than, say, discussing a project in which we are both involved. I love my friends but socialising is just very difficult.

I find that **I can feel less lonely when I communicate with people for a reason.** Just talking to a colleague about the work we are doing makes me feel less lonely, because we have our work as a common theme.

Interacting with my colleagues because we are working on the same project and aiming to achieve the same awesome things can be very enjoyable. I like collaborating with someone on a project where we are both working separately to achieve the same common goal:

Separate Work → **Shared Goal**

It is hard for me to work so closely with someone as I like to do things in my own way, at my own pace and to work things out for myself. I do not like collaborating with someone on a project when we are working on it at the same time, in the same physical space and having to talk to each other:

Sharing Work → **Shared Goal**

Working with The Curly Hair Project Trainers has been a good way of collaborating because they do the training (which is very separate from what I do) and I do my work (which is very separate from what they do), yet we all contribute towards The Curly Hair Project. Similarly, working from home doing assignments set by my other managers means I do the work completely independently of my managers and colleagues, but the work is still required by them. I like working on team or big projects (even if they are someone else's) because they make me feel connected to people, but I need my contribution to be completely separate.

Feelings

I have noticed that there is an issue with the emotional lack of connection when I speak with someone, regardless of whether they are a friend or a colleague. **I can have a conversation with someone with very little anxiety when there is something to be done or when there is a purpose,** but talking about *feelings* make me feel uncomfortable. In some ways a relationship with a colleague is easier than a relationship with a friend because I can relate to my colleagues through work rather than through emotion.

When there is a task to be done we can work out how to do the task and we can each then follow the steps in our separate ways. However, as soon as anyone asks me, "How are you feeling?" or asks me about my personal life, I start to feel uncomfortable. The answer is usually that I am feeling stressed! Also, when someone says to me "I feel [emotion]", I am not always sure how to respond and that makes me feel nervous. But if someone said to me "Can you do [task]?" I would be fine.

I understand that people have a need to talk about their feelings, however I will usually only be able to respond very factually or practically or I will not say much at all. Of course, I care about how someone is feeling and I will listen to their problems and come away from the interaction knowing how they are feeling (sometimes this is all people want) but actually responding to them by saying something is very hard.

I prefer not to talk to people about my own feelings as I know that they are atypical and I worry they will not respond in the way I need (the wrong response can make me feel worse). Sometimes it is just because talking does not make me feel good and it does not come easily to me anyway. If I am already feeling a bit low, talking about a situation can actually intensify the emotion rather than keep it hidden away.

Looking back through my life, I realise that one of the reasons why I have struggled to have friends is because I find it very hard to connect with them emotionally. Talking about feelings is hard. Identifying feelings is hard. Relating to the experiences of others is hard. Giving the 'right' sympathetic or empathetic sort of response to others is also hard.

It is only since learning about ASD and coming to understand myself better, combined with increased awareness of ASD in the wider world generally that I have felt more able to emotionally connect with people. It is now easier for me to talk about my emotions than it once was.

Using social media

The use of social media has been a blessing for many autistic people who would otherwise find it impossible to have friends and maintain relationships. There are many autistic people I know who love to use social media. I am probably a bit different as I do not really use social media for personal reasons. I am too introverted, have too much social anxiety, too many social communication difficulties and just generally feel too much of an observer inside my glass jar to ever be able to interact with people in this way. I go through life with that nagging feeling of always being on the outside looking in and that does not change because I am on the internet.

Social media is, however, a useful tool to see what other people have been, or are, doing. It is easy to know what your friends are doing, even if you do not see or talk to them because their stories and photos are right there on your screen. I can feel quite involved with someone's life even if I never see them in person or talk to them individually. I understand how it can be a less anxiety-provoking way to stay connected to people. You can feel connected to someone even if all you ever do is read or hear about their life without ever commenting or sharing anything about yours (although I am a bit unusual, as everyone who knows me and my work can always see what I have been doing anyway as it is all over the internet all the time!). It's also quite helpful to have all the information about those you know in one place!

I have mixed feelings about how I use social media. The more I think about it, the more I start to feel that I have better relationships with people who I see more often face to face. I personally find it more difficult to maintain relationships with people who I know through solely communicating online.

Friendships

I have learned that sometimes **what we think we want is not what we actually want.** For example I used to think that I wanted lots of friends. Now I think that what I more accurately wanted was:

1) to fit in and enjoy friendships in the same, easy, natural way that everyone else does
2) to connect to at least one person.

With regards to point 1, to be in a social situation where everybody else is making friends and I am not is an excruciatingly painful experience. To have that ability to join in and make friends would be wonderful. I also used to feel jealous of people who have friends (I still do sometimes) because I can see people and how they are with each other and I can see them having fun and sharing experiences. I would love to be able to share in that experience, but my ASD means that I am not able to. I have tried, so it is not because of a lack of trying. I have participated in many social situations and I have done a fair amount of socialising but I never get to the same the level of connection with people that they experience with each other.

Now, I understand and accept that I am not this way. Fitting in and enjoying a social situation does not happen often. I can encourage it to happen using the strategies I have talked about in this book but I accept that it is a forced situation rather than a natural one.

Point 2 about connecting to at least one person has come about because going through life not really having any real friendships has led to severe loneliness. I believe that **finding just one person that I could connect with** is what I wanted when I was younger. Having just one special person would have helped me so much.

Since leaving education, and getting out of full time employment, I have found it much easier to find people I can relate to. I am not as exhausted in daily life. I have the energy to meet people, and be in control about who I am seeing as opposed to just being around lots of people, all day every day, who I have nothing in common with other than that they were my classmates or are my work colleagues.

I have met people in cafés, on dog walks and on dating websites. I have met people through The Curly Hair Project. I made a friend because I contacted someone who put a very clear advert in the local newsagent shop window that read <I am looking for someone to go dog walking and have picnics with>

The friends I have now were nurtured from the outset, by outright asking for people's phone numbers and making the effort to arrange to meet them. After that these relationships have actually developed relatively naturally for me. I just had to make the first move.

Conditions

I do put some 'conditions' on any relationship because otherwise they just cause me to feel stressed. I have learned that I have to be careful about any relationship I build, because it can easily become more stressful than enjoyable. I have narrowed it down to four conditions and when I look for friends, these are the things that matter to me:

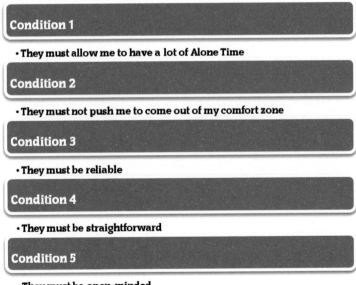

Condition 1
- They must allow me to have a lot of Alone Time

Condition 2
- They must not push me to come out of my comfort zone

Condition 3
- They must be reliable

Condition 4
- They must be straightforward

Condition 5
- They must be open-minded

Condition 1: The person must allow me to have a lot of Alone Time.
I need a lot of space. The people I know who understand about autism do have some understanding of why I keep to myself. It is the hardest thing about my relationships because I can go weeks, months, sometimes years,

without speaking or seeing somebody that I care about. Even though I really like them it just never feels like the right time to make contact or to meet up. We can go for a long period of time without meeting and yet I still have that feeling "It's not the right time at the moment". That can be hard because, unless the other person has some understanding of autism, they find it tough to have a relationship with someone like me.

I like my friends, but I still lack the desire and motivation to socialise and spend as much time with them as they might like. I just need my own company and to do my own thing most of the time. Maybe I am just worried about being so tired after seeing someone that I will not be able to do my own things as well as I would normally. Maybe I just genuinely do find socialising extremely difficult and that is all there is to it. There are lots of reasons but nothing is ever meant personally. I think my friends are lovely and I love them, but I am very introverted with a very complex disability.

Ultimately, I think I just prefer being on my own or just only being around the 'right' people at the 'right' time.

Disclaimer: Of course, I may want people to be there for me in my time of need, so I have to allow a bit of give and take, but mostly I tend to see or do things with people to fulfil *their* social needs rather than mine. I will also always try to be there for someone if they need me, as long as they tell me they do - as I will not be able to read the signs or intuitively understand their needs!

(I have learned that I sometimes just have to take the leap and go and see someone because, if I do not, I perhaps never will. A lot of the time there is just never a 'good time'. If I value a relationship I have learned that **I will have to force myself to see the person occasionally.**)

I need people to be very patient (and as I said, it can take me months or years for a relationship to work out) and a lot of the time I might never be able to get to that level with them. An example of this might be someone I know - but do not spend much time with - trying to connect with me by inviting me out, but I just never seem to feel up to doing it.

It is interesting looking back over my life, as I remember that I was always this way, always highly introverted and always had a lack of motivation to spend time with others. Most of the people around me caused me to feel I was 'wrong' and that I 'should' be having more friends and be more sociable, even if it never felt intrinsically right. I am glad that there is more understanding and awareness of autism now. I think the world might be becoming more accepting of introversion and autism (just to be clear I do not think introversion and autism are the same, but there is overlap and I happen to be both).

When I am busy, I have no interest or energy for socialising with anyone. Should my social energy tank be empty, I can go days, weeks and months without anyone hearing from me. This has been something difficult to deal with, especially in relation to my work and the people I care about. There is an expectation to be responsive, caring and helpful, and meeting that expectation is hard a lot of the time. I think that when I meet someone who is not used to dealing with an autistic person, it can be very difficult for them to understand how I can be very sociable and chatty one day, but completely silent and withdrawn the next. Actually, usually it is *because* I have been so sociable and chatty one day that I have to spend the following days being quiet on my own.

Time to recharge is something that all people who have relations with someone with ASD, will need to get used to. There will be times where the autistic person will want to be left alone. I wish more people understood that it is not a personal attack against them when this happens. **I actually really like a lot of people but I need a lot of space too.**

Condition 2: They must not push me to come out of my comfort zone.
Condition 2 is a reinforcement of the fact that, in order for me to function in this world, I have to stick to situations that I find comfortable. I have a set of "safe" or "familiar" activities and situations that I can cope with, so a friend has to be happy doing only these things and not putting pressure on me to do something different. They can always ask me, but **I cannot cope with anyone pushing me or trying to persuade me to do something that I am not comfortable with.**

So for example, I will be comfortable walking my dog with Friend A but will not necessarily feel comfortable to go to Friend A's house; or I will be comfortable meeting Friend B for a cup of tea in a coffee shop but I will not necessarily feel comfortable going to the theatre with Friend B. Or I will be comfortable working with Friend C on an assignment, but will not necessarily feel comfortable doing anything outside of that. I like to be asked and given the choice, but any 'pushing' will put me off the person completely.

Condition 3: They must be reliable.
Reliability is something that I seek to find in another person. I cannot

cope with people who are unreliable or too casual about what they are doing, especially when it involves me. Because my own world is so carefully thought out and meticulously planned, if I am to involve someone else that person has to fit in smoothly. Remember that we have our separate worlds but together we will have a shared world and I do not want that shared world disorganised, unpredictable and chaotic. It has to be kept orderly and calm.

I like someone who is always on time, does what they say they are going to do, and works to a schedule that they create for themselves. I notice that some people go through life without communicating much detail – for example what their plans are, why they are doing what they are doing. Sometimes they do not communicate this because they do not actually know the detail themselves. I find it really hard to have a relationship with someone who is this way inclined – their vague and casual approach does not fit well into my world, so unless they can consciously change themselves to fit in with me, it is unlikely that I will get on with them.

I have one friend who is very clear and direct about when she is going to see me and what we are going to do. She is very reliable when she is with me. I appreciate her efforts. However, she openly admits that her natural way is to not be like that at all. Indeed, she said if her friends knew that she was always on time when she met me they would not believe it, because they know her as someone who is always late! This is an example of someone who I get on well with because she has been able to adapt to my needs, even though in normal circumstances she is known to be very casual and laid back. She respected my world by keeping our shared world how I need it to be.

Condition 4: They must be straightforward.
I can only have friendships with people who are very straightforward. This means that they do not:

1) 'read between the lines' of the actions I take and comments I say (with me, there are never any 'in between the lines'):

2) create 'in between the lines' expecting that I will be able to interpret the point they are making:

I go about my daily life in a very logical, straightforward manner and generally do not have any negative intentions towards anyone. If I do or say something that someone has taken in a negative way I probably did it because: 1) it made sense to me, or 2) I did not realise it could be taken that way. I can only have friendships with people who recognise this about me and therefore understand that I very rarely would have any bad feelings towards anyone. I am not able to have relationships with people who create emotional 'drama' from things that they have assumed or made up rather than what I have *actually* said or done.

For example, let me introduce you to my Friend A and my Friend B.

Friend A: <Hi, would you like to meet up?>
Me: <No, I'm bit tired, but thank you for asking>
Friend A: <OK, that's not a problem. Hope to see you soon. Just let me know when you fancy it xx>

Friend A took me at my word. This sort of conversation has far less of an anxiety-provoking effect on me than a conversation with Friend B:

Friend B: <Hi, would you like to meet up?>
Me: <No, I'm a bit tired, but thank you for asking>
Friend B: <Oh that's a shame, I haven't seen you for ages. [Insert statement such as "You're always busy!" or "You must stop working so much!" or even worse "Have I done something wrong?" or "You're always tired! What's wrong?"]>

This conversation seems to create some emotional 'drama'. This sort of reply is likely to make me feel very anxious.

The interesting thing here is that, Friend A who sent the first message, is far more likely to hear from me and see me sooner. I would probably respond to them very quickly. Friend B, who sent the second message, is someone who I would find it difficult to respond to. I would probably take a long time to reply or maybe not reply at all. I would also be put off seeing them in person.

I am very direct. I say exactly what I mean. In these messages, I was honest and told them each that I was feeling tired. That was all there was to it. So why Friend B has to make more of it than it is when talking to me is beyond me, as I am completely straightforward when I talk to others.

I think this fits in nicely with my view that many people make assumptions and interpret things that they think are implied and not actually said.

If we think back to the example just mentioned, Friend A who was very direct and straightforward would think nothing of what I said. They would take me at my word that I was tired and did not want to meet up. Friend B, on the other hand, would probably come up with his or her own conclusion about my response, such as that I did not like her, that I was making excuses, that there was something wrong because I did not want to see her or that I was not interested. None of those things were what I had actually said. I had told her that I was tired and did not feel like meeting up and that was all there is to it.

I find it difficult to communicate with people who make too many assumptions about me or who interpret my words in the way they want to interpret rather than what I actually say. It happens far less now because my social circle is so small and selective… but when I was at university and school, around a lot of people, these sorts of misunderstanding happened all the time.

Similarly, I can only have good relationships with people who do not create 'in between the lines' for me. They tell me explicitly what they want from me, if I have upset them in any way, and just generally do not expect me to be able to read their mind. Let us go back to another example of Friend A and Friend B who have been unwell.

Friend B: <Hi Alis. I've been really unwell>
Me: <I'm really sorry to hear that. Can I do anything?>
Friend B: <No>

I later find out that Friend B was upset with me because I did not visit her. In comparison:

Friend A: <Hi Alis. I've been really unwell. Would you be able to come and visit me?>
Me: <I'm really sorry to hear that. Yes, of course>

It took a long time for Friend B to tell me that she was upset with me and, even after I had apologised, there still seemed to be some 'tension'. This to me is just emotional drama, which I cannot deal with. I need people to be very direct and if there is ever an 'issue', such as Friend B becoming upset, I want it to be talked about and resolved quickly and for us to move on.

Condition 5: They must be open-minded.
Some of my best friends are the complete opposite of me, and some I have little in common with, but we still connect so well. It made me really think about why these relationships are successful.

Is it more about how we both think about something and whether we ask the same sort of questions and think in the same way? Do we have something similar that we wish to talk about? If their thought processes are similar to mine I will get on well with them, regardless of how different their lifestyle and interests are. If their thought processes are not like mine, but they are open minded and patient enough to listen, understand me, and predict the sorts of questions I might ask, the relationship is also likely to work.

These 'conditions' are not personal restrictions on friends exactly, they are more to do the difficulties I have with sensory processing, anxiety, social energy, executive function and being out of routine.

Those are the conditions I set myself for anyone who I plan on getting close to. I have not specifically made them clear to any of my friends because they are implicit in our relationship and because the people I intrinsically gravitate towards are naturally empathetic and understanding, so I never have to make these conditions clear. They figure them out for themselves.

So I have managed to make a small number of friends. I care about them a lot, but they accept that our relationship might be limited. My friends understand.

Finding the right people to be around is important. These are the people I want to build a relationship with. A person might not initially be someone that I want to be in a relationship with me but they can become that person, if they are willing to learn a bit about me.

The ideal sort of companionship looks like this:

Not everyone will meet all these criteria, but meeting just one of these can help so much.

Having a relationship with someone who meets these conditions helps me so much to feel connected and to feel as though I have a true friend. Just having one person who understands me will stop me from feeling lonely. Even if I do not speak to or see my friends often, the actual relationships I have with them are meaningful and fulfilling because of the *way* we are together and this gives me enjoyment rather than stress.

What companion makes the right company?

- Likes working on mutual projects or doing routine activities
- Empathetic, understanding, straightforward personality type and an open mind
- Happy to have minimal interaction
- Happy to communicate using email/text
- Is clear, concise, direct, to the point when they communicate
- Gives structure (purpose to interaction, clear end time)

For example, having a relationship with someone who has no issue with seeing me infrequently, who is happy to text or email and to do activities with me that are inside my comfort zone, who allows me my space, who encourages me to do my weightlifting, etc. will all give enjoyment. In the past I have had relationships with people who do not understand me and this makes me feel stressed, making the relationship meaningless (this was not necessarily the other person's fault. Much of it was down to me not having my ASD diagnosis, and not understanding myself very well, not conveying my needs clearly and disguising all of this by masking in order to fit in).

I have a lot more confidence nowadays to say outright to someone "I would rather not do that" [because of my ASD] or "Is there any way we could compromise or adapt this please?" as opposed to being passive and going along with something that makes me feel too uncomfortable. **I have only been able to develop meaningful relationships with people because I tell them about my ASD.**

Wishing for conventional relationships

I do wish that I did not have to have such conditions about making relationships. If it was not like this life would be a lot easier for me and for those around me, because I would have a normal capability for making and maintaining relationships. I would not have to always give an explanation about my need to be alone and that my lack of contact is nothing personal. I would not be as lonely if I could enjoy normal relationships with people.

I always observe how other people are when they are with their friends and I hear people talk about their friendships, which can be a bit of a surreal experience. I just do not "get" it. I am not able to experience or understand how they are connecting. It is a very disconcerting and lonely way to go through life and extremely strange to explain to others. Most people have friendships and enjoy spending time with their friends, so to imagine my own strange experiences must be difficult.

Sunny day and pub example

This is an example of something that happened to me when I was having a group text chat with my colleagues, one of whom was leaving the veterinary practice where I worked. The colleague had arranged a get-together at a pub one sunny evening. Everyone was invited. I was reading their plans and sensing their happiness about the evening out but I could not connect with them. I actually spent several days ruminating over what the evening might be like and what they would be talking about.

Shared interests

A good starting point for anyone wanting to build a relationship is to find something that they have in common with someone else. However, I have noticed that, for me, this strategy only works a very small percentage of the time. This is because I am quite private and prefer to keep my interests to myself, either because my interests are uncommon or because the way I think about and pursue my interests are different from most people. For example, talking about weightlifting to someone who also likes weightlifting, but who likes it in a different way, can end up leaving me feeling frustrated or isolated:

Osteopath and gym example

My osteopath works in two practices, the practice that I go to and another practice which is located in a brand new gym. When I visit for an osteopathy session he talks to me about how "awesome" the gym is there and says that I "would love it" and that I "should go and train there some time"! He shows me photos of the equipment and videos of some of the lifters in action. I understand that he is trying to be nice and connect with me through something that we have in common (he lifts weights too), but I have no interest in training at that gym. In fact, the idea of training in that particular gym fills me with dread!

This challenge is to do with the 'social interaction' impairment of autism which is: *having different interests and viewing life in a different way.* It is not just my interests that are unusual it is the way I pursue them too.

For example, I might tell someone that I do weightlifting and their response might be, "Which gym do you train at?", and as soon as I tell them that I train at home their interest tends to vanish as they cannot relate to training at home. They enjoy going to their own gym, being around other people, participating in the classes, using all the super equipment available and seeing other people lift huge weights...etc. (This is an example. Some people think that it is awesome that I have a gym at home!) I have dated some people who do not exercise but want to get into it in order to connect with me using this as a means. They say "Which gym do you go to? I could come to your gym with you". If it is someone I do not yet know well then it is a bit awkward to invite them into my home to use my gym, but if I used a public gym it would be easier.

A further example could be telling someone that I really enjoy a particular pizza at a particular restaurant. Their response might be, "Great. I like that restaurant too. Would you like to go some time?" Although I really like the restaurant, and I can see that the person is trying to find something in common with me, it is not as simple as me saying yes, choosing a date and going to the restaurant. I have to consider the whole situation as well, such as managing my social energy and fitting it into my routine.

I have difficulty staying friends with people who I used to have something in common with me but now no longer do. Whereas I find that other people's interests change, my interests tend not to change. I can think about someone who I used to be quite close to because we had shared interest, but now they no longer have that same shared interest and this means that I can no longer relate to them.

Regular routine

Another strategy I have learned is to **make someone a part of my regular routine.** If I see someone on the same day and at the same time it helps me to maintain a relationship. Walking the dogs with my friend once a week is a good way. A friend coming to my house in the evenings to watch the same TV programme is a good way.

A regular routine that I am unable to avoid, such as walking my dog, helps me maintain contact with people. The relationship might not develop otherwise, because it is more difficult and confusing to know when, and how, to meet up with someone regularly. If it is part of a routine this difficulty is avoided.

Situations that involve work and education are excellent for maintaining relationships with people because both involve predictable routine including when and how I am going to interact with them. It is really hard when these situations end because I find that these relationships tend to dissolve. I really miss the people but find I can no longer interact with them easily.

There is also a lot more effort required to see someone and stay in touch. All of this makes maintaining a relationship stressful, rather than enjoyable. Some of the best relationships I have had have been phase-specific but it does mean that they are likely to be short-term. For example, a friendship might last only as long as we are both in the same job or a friendship might only last as long as we are both on the same course.

I do however realise now that certain relationships are very important to me and I know that I am happier in life because I do have relationships, so **I try to see people** regardless of circumstances, even if it is hard.

I find it hard to keep in touch with someone when the routine we have no longer coincides. For example, I used to see my friend at a coffee shop in the morning because we both happened to go there (with or without the intention of meeting up with each other). I no longer go to the coffee shop in the morning so I no longer see her there. I try to keep in touch, but our relationship has definitely changed. We do meet up sometimes but it feels a lot more 'forced' (because it has been arranged and because we have both had to make an effort to meet rather than our paths crossing naturally like they used to). This then makes the socialising more difficult and more anxiety-provoking. It is not meant to sound contradictory that I enjoyed our more spontaneous interaction (because previously I said I needed a lot of planning beforehand!) but even though these were spontaneous they were also quite predictable. This friend of mine is very easy going, so even if we were both in the coffee shop at the same time, it did not mean we felt we had to talk to each other. She always used to say "Do you want to chat today, or would you rather not?" Similarly, if she told me that she did not want to chat today, it was not a big deal.

At one of the places that I worked I was close to two of my colleagues. I really enjoyed talking to them at work. However, when I left the job, I really struggled to maintain my relationship with them (even though we had a really nice relationship). We all liked eating pizza and met up at a restaurant a few times. It was OK but it was not the same. I wonder whether **keeping a relationship 'the same' is more important to me than it being 'enjoyable'.** The difficulty is that life constantly changes and so it is impossible to keep most relationships the same. We just talked less and less until eventually the contact was gone.

Something else I have noticed is that if I do not see or talk to people very often, when I do see them, any change (not necessarily in their appearance – but their present activities) that I notice feels so much more drastic and is more anxiety-provoking. Seeing someone on a regular basis means I probably will not even notice the changes, as these are evolutionary.

Had I kept in touch more frequently with my university friend, meeting him would not have distressed me as much. Maybe I would not have even bothered to meet him as our relationship may have slowly ended anyway before he 'changed'.

One to one socialising

I have learned that a successful social life for me is **spending time with one other person** and getting to know them. I generally will not want to meet their network of friends or be involved in their social life. So for example, I will have a relationship walking my dog with a friend... but if that friend invited me to a party or to meet their family, I would find that difficult.

I also find that people, including myself, change when other people are around and I find it difficult to figure out the different personas they are showing. If a friend acts differently from what I am used to that can make me feel lonely, because I feel as though I do not know them as well as I thought.

Once I was enjoying a relationship with someone that I had met while out walking. It started because she had stopped me when I was out with my puppy and said, "I've just got a puppy too! Do you want to come over sometime so that they can play with each other?" I went over to her house a few times and we got on really well (and our dogs had a lot of fun too!). On one occasion, without warning, I arrived at her house as planned and there were lots of other people, including her family and friends, visiting. I felt really disconnected and lonely as they were all chatting comfortably and having fun, but I just could not participate due to my anxiety and ASD. My friend also behaved differently from what I had been used to.

The loneliest times of my life have been the times when I have been around other people who seem to get on well with each other and I feel on the outside. Large gatherings at parties, work, university, etc. all feel too chaotic and are the worst for making me feel lonely. I decline an invitation to any group social activity because I know that it will make me feel worse. Not only am I unusual, which means that I do not naturally fit in, but I have too many social impairments to be able to keep up with a group conversation. At least if I am on my own with just one other person I only have to pay attention to them.

The sensory input that people generate is another factor that makes being with lots of people tiring and overwhelming. If there is only one person then I have to process only that one person's smell, the colours or patterns on their clothes, their movement and the sound of their voice. However, in a group the sensory input is all magnified. In a one to one situation I just have to understand one person's voice and body language (as in the way they intonate, the volume of their voice, how they move their hands and make gestures, etc.) and that is complicated enough, but to have to do that with multiple people all at once is beyond me!

Educating others

I have learned that teaching others helps me feel as though I have relationships. The creation of The Curly Hair Project has enabled me to do this because I write books and blog articles, publish memes, develop training courses and direct films that teach other people about autism.

The way I am means that I could never be a teacher nor have any sort of conventional job that involved coaching or directly supporting others but, despite my difficulties, I have still managed to find ways to teach that I find comfortable. If you have known me for a long time you might know that I initially carried out some of the autism training for The Curly Hair Project myself. Immediately realising it was not for me, I was able to devise a training side to The Curly Hair Project that allows Trainers to train, leaving me in my comfort zone of writing, filmmaking and other creative projects.

Before I started the CHP I did not realise how important and how rewarding teaching could be. Not only does my work help *others* feel less lonely, I too feel far more connected to the world and as a consequence less lonely because I share my knowledge with other people. **I wonder whether other autistic people might feel less lonely if they were able to teach others.**[6]

Before I developed the CHP, I had lots of information in my head (for example: my autism and how it affects me), but did not share it with anyone. Why would I? Previously, when I had verbally shared my thoughts and feelings with people, they had not been able to understand or relate to me, or they had shrugged off the points I was making, or worse still, they tried to ridicule or bully me.

I am not very sociable and I am not a talker, so sharing this information through daily conversation is not particularly meaningful. There are also very few people who want to hear me talk about autism. Autism, as a subject matter, is rather specialised so I cannot easily tell anyone about how I think and what I have learned about it. By creating a community of people, through writing and training my Trainers, who are interested

---

6 Rowe, A (2018). Asperger's Syndrome: Socialising & Social Energy. 2nd ed. London: Lonely Mind Books. 63–67.

in autism, I feel connected and less lonely. Autism is like weightlifting… not many people will be particularly interested in hearing about it… so you just have to find who those people are!

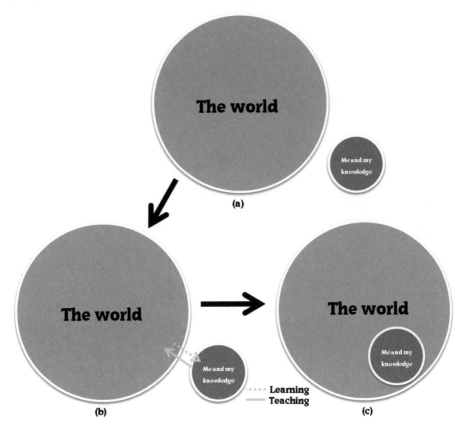

(a) If you have a lot of thoughts, feelings or knowledge in your head, but never share it with anyone, you can feel very disconnected. (b) By sharing that knowledge with other people by teaching them, it may start to make you feel more connected. Learning from other people can also help. (c) When your knowledge is being used and appreciated by other people, you are likely to feel connected to the world.

Summary of what I have learned about socialising and relationships:

- Small talk is important – keep it honest and brief
- Understand Social Energy Theory
- Understand the true meaning of being an introvert
- Ensure you have time for recharging (whatever that is for you – for me it is being alone) and make maintaining this time a priority
- Consistent Alone Time to recharge, for me, means more energy available to maintain relationships
- Be a good listener
- Talk to people who are genuinely interested in what I am interested in, or who have an open mind to want to learn more
- It is best to find a good balance between being neurotypical and being autistic (rather than masking all the time)
- Socialise with people as part of a structured routine
- Socialise with people for a purpose
- Socialise with people regularly
- Try not to talk about my own emotions unless with the 'right' person at the right time
- Use social media to keep in touch with friends
- Decide what I truly want from friends, not what I think I should want (my conditions are: someone who allows me a lot of Alone Time, is happy to do the same things, and is reliable and straightforward and open minded)
- Educating others helps me feel more connected to people

WHAT i HAVE LEARNED ABOUT BEiNG DiFFERENT

Abilities and deficits
A gift?
Reducing the feeling of difference

Abilities and deficits

The reason ASD is called a developmental disability is because the brain develops differently. I accept that I am different but, most of the time I hate *feeling* that I am.

I would really, really like to say that being different is awesome and amazing but I do not truly think it is. I am not, unfortunately, an autistic person who feels proud of and happy about their differences. I certainly have some unique skills and ways of thinking that are awesome and amazing but the consequences of having these is that: 1) connecting with people is extremely hard and 2) general day to day life is enormously difficult and at times terrifying – as the world is set up for neurotypicals, not for people like me. The two consequences have led to very intense feelings of loneliness, confusion and anxiety and very dark periods of depression.

Being different in a world that is geared towards those who are neurotypical *does* put you at a disadvantage. The abilities required to get by and succeed in daily life also happen to be my challenges. For example, neurotypical people might already have the following abilities (and many more!):

- Executive function including adaptability (the ability to be flexible to changes and situations that are not planned)
- Sensory processing (the ability to feel physically comfortable)
- Social energy (the desire to interact with other people) and social skills

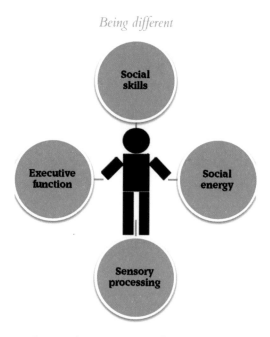

These are the same things that are normally impaired or limited in autistic people.

Adaptability is very important and it is the ability to adapt to change, cope with spontaneity and to be resilient. So, for example, if I turn up at work one day and my manager informs me that my desk had been temporarily moved, it would make me feel very anxious. A neurotypical person might feel a tiny bit of anxiety but then would quickly think nothing further and they would go to their new desk and just get on with their day. In contrast, I would probably feel highly anxious and upset for the whole day, which would, in turn, affect my performance at work.

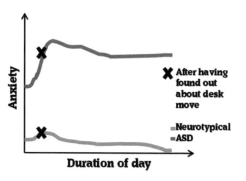

Social abilities are similar. A neurotypical person will most likely be able to get through social situations and their flexible thinking and inherent social skills will mean they will be able to resolve any problems. For example, if someone goes into a shop and cannot find the particular item, they will simply ask the shop assistant for help. Something as basic as this is really hard for me to do and often means I leave the shop without getting what I want.

I can tell that some neurotypical people might be shyer or quieter than others, but I can also see that they are still able to collaborate with the people around them. I am thinking back to my school and university days. I can think of a few people who were a bit more introverted or shyer than average, but when it came to needing to function as part of the group (for example, laboratory work, group assignments), they still seemed to manage and they were included. I am not like this – I am not normally included and cannot seem to function.

I will talk about *sensory processing* in more detail later. Most neurotypical people are not overly physically uncomfortable in a 'normal' situation such as in the supermarket, shopping centre, cinema or workplace. These situations can be so loud, bright, smelly and crowded that I cannot bear to be in them.

(Disclaimer: It is important to note however, that my observations are observations only. You can never truly know how someone else is experiencing something. There are no facts to back up what I am describing. It might be that the people I mention, who looked on the surface shy and quiet, also had very severe social difficulties and went home feeling exhausted every single time. They may also have absolutely dreaded the idea of having to work with other people. I am unlikely to ever find out unless I ask and, even then, what one person considers to be "dread" or "social exhaustion" can be completely different from what someone else experiences as "dread" or "social exhaustion".)

It is easy to say that if an autistic person's skills are made use of then this can benefit society. The problem is that an autistic person's skills are only likely to be utilised if the other people around them can maintain the environment that is optimal for these skills to be utilised. Other people can easily do this on one occasion, but to *maintain* the need to adapt seems really hard because it does not feel natural. Here are two examples:

Imagine that I work in a job that has a regular team meeting, for which there never seems to be an agenda. I have some excellent ideas and my manager respects me for being an innovator. I can only speak about my ideas and suggestions in meetings *if* I know beforehand what we are going to be discussing. The manager makes note of this and she makes it a rule that, from now on, for every meeting there will be an agenda. This works well for the first few meetings and I am able to participate very well and give some very helpful ideas and suggestions. As time goes on however, the need for having an agenda is forgotten, making it difficult for me to put forward my ideas.

Imagine that I work in a job that is very busy and chaotic. My manager understands that I need a quiet space in order to do my work so he arranges for me to able to use a particular room where no one will disturb me. He also makes other colleagues aware of this arrangement. I work very well in this quiet space. However, over time, the need for me to have that alone, quiet time is forgotten and either other colleagues start using the room or my manager starts disturbing me, making it impossible for me to concentrate.

A gift?

Unfortunately, I do not consider my ASD to be a gift, and I would rather not have the condition. When I describe myself as being 'different', I do mean that I am different, but it is also clear to me that I have a disability (I understand that lots of autistic people do not consider themselves to be disabled, but I do).

I always used to think I was just very shy, and that was the trait that made me different, but now I know it was a lot more. ASD affects how I experience every aspect of life and is not just to do with socialising.

In order to feel less different **I spend a lot of time alone and a lot of time at home.**

I experience that isolating feeling of being different more or less every time I am with other people or in a public place. A simple example of this would be going to the train station and being in the situation when the train is late. I can see that the train is due to arrive at 12:01 yet the time now is 12:03 and the train has still not arrived. I can sense that other people are not put out by this, but *I am.* Inside I am very, very confused and anxious wondering why the sign has not updated and how late is the train going to be? I fixate on the sign. I realise I cannot be certain how other people are feeling, but from speaking with my family and friends, I have been told that a train being late by one or two minutes probably would not irritate them because they are used to it and understand that it will shortly arrive. It is unlikely that they would even notice whether or not the sign was reflecting the correct time. But I fixate on the sign and what time it is showing versus what the time is.

So my experience of this situation, which is not even a 'social' one, it is just catching a train, still makes me feel different because I am experiencing it differently.

Another example would be when I am at the theatre with my family.

126

If the play is supposed to start at 2.30pm, then that is that time I am expecting it to start. When it does not start on time, I begin to feel very anxious that the play might now end late and that the rest of the day's routine will get disturbed. But when I look at all the people around me, including my own family, no one else appears to be concerned about the time. They are all talking and laughing and they look very happy rather than anxious like me.

Whenever I go to my favourite restaurant, I always order the same dish from the menu and that includes a side salad without tomatoes and without dressing. I have been going to this restaurant for years, always ordering the same side salad, and always receiving it as I expected. Once the waiter brought me my side salad without tomatoes and without dressing, but with black pepper sprinkled over it. I had not expected this and black pepper was not mentioned on the menu either. But no one else at my table seemed to notice that the side salad had changed and had come sprinkled with black pepper. When I asked my dad whether he could send it back for me and ask for another without black pepper, he said to me, "You'll hardly be able to taste it. Can't you just have it the way it is please?" This situation made me feel so different and lonely because the problem was not even considered a problem by anyone else.

Another example I can remember at college, is that one of our teachers did not have very good written English. He wrote something on the whiteboard with an apostrophe in the wrong place. All I could think about and focus on in that lesson was that apostrophe and why he had not corrected his mistake. Nobody else commented on this. I just sat there and wondered why no one else had noticed or had not pointed out the mistake. No one seemed to care yet it became the entire focus of the lesson for me. Again, it was another example of me feeling 'different' which was not related to 'socialising'.

> <u>Xylem cell's</u>
>
> • Carry dissolved minerals
> • Support the plant

It did not even matter to me what xylem cells actually did. All that mattered in this particular lesson was the apostrophe in the wrong place.

(Disclaimer: Once again, you could say that I do not actually know for sure whether other people were not bothered or had not noticed the incorrect apostrophe. I am basing these thoughts on the evidence I have gathered when talking to neurotypical friends about how they experience the world. They have said that it is unlikely that they would notice an incorrect apostrophe and, if they did notice, they would not say anything.)

Our dog had an 'accident' in the house. We cleaned up very thoroughly and the rest of my family thought that all was now fine. However, I could still smell that it was not quite clean. But no one else could. Although my mum emphasised that it was probably a very good thing that I was able to smell that it was not quite clean so that we could carry on cleaning, the fact that no one else noticed was just another reminder that I am different.

I once had an appointment to have a blood test with a nurse at my GP. The nurse had been informed that I was autistic in advance of the appointment, and I also reminded her of this again when I arrived. However, despite this, she gave lots and lots of eye contact, she touched me on the arm in order to comfort me, and she told me to "close my eyes and to imagine being somewhere relaxing". These gestures all made me feel worse. But obviously the reason why she did these things is because she felt that it must help most patients in the same situation. It was another reminder that I am different.

Reducing the feeling of difference

Being at home is really the primary way that I can stop feeling different because I am reminded that I am different in *every* public situation. The fact that I have to ask people to make 'reasonable adjustments' also reminds me that I am different. Of course, I only ask for the adjustments to be made because I benefit from them. But I always wish that I was able to cope well in non-adjusted situations.

There is no real way that I can stop feeling different in a public place, because the world is set up in such a neurotypical-friendly way that no matter where I am, or what I do, I do not fit in. Being in places that have tried to be 'autism-friendly' might help but I wish they did not need to explicitly say they are autism-friendly, **they just need to be open minded, good communicators and considerate** of all people (something I feel very strongly about is that 'autism-friendly' is, a lot of the time, just 'human-friendly'. Many of the reasonable adjustments that are supposed to help autistic people can help the rest of society as well).

There is a lot to be done in society to make life better for someone who is different without having to highlight the fact that they are. I do not want 'autism-friendliness' to be made obvious, I just think that all places could be a lot more 'human-friendly'! I truly believe that the CHP work is very important in helping people to be a bit more aware and considerate of someone who may not be like them. Regardless of whether or not you are autistic, or whether you know someone who is autistic, the CHP will help you see and think about things in a different way, which can help you be a more open minded and considerate individual.

Thinking about the positive aspects of autism that I have is a nice thing to do but, unfortunately, it is still another reminder that I am different. However utilising these skills in daily life has made a big difference to my self-confidence. For example, I have managed to find work that I am very, very good at (*because* of my differences). I have found a sport that I love and am very good at (no doubt *because* of the traits ASD has given me).

I try to avoid group situations as much as possible (unless there is some diversity within that group). If most people in a group are more similar to each other than I am to any of them (which is always the case), I just feel too different.

When I am in the presence of others, I can *see* that I am different because of the way that others behave and because of how and what they talk about to each other. It is different from how I behave and how I think. I can pretend to be similar ('masking'), but this is exhausting and makes me feel completely disconnected from myself. When I am alone there is no one to compare myself with, so the way I behave and think is the only way there is and it is normal, so I do not feel different.

Observing other people having fun, talking, laughing and connecting with one another is the loneliest of feelings. They are participating and I am observing. They are all getting the same enjoyment from one another's company. I am not. Sometimes even when I am with several people who, individually, I consider to be my friends, I always feel that they get on with each other better than they do with me and that can make me feel lonely:

Spending time with people who are similar to each other, not just in terms of their interests, but in the way they think, makes it obvious to me that most people think differently from me and that they think more similarly to each other. Their similarities mean that my difference is magnified:

I can feel a bit less different if all members of a group act as individuals rather than crowd-followers:

I can feel less different if I spend time with individuals who are 'outsiders' (people who have something a bit different about them). I actually already used this strategy intuitively when I was at school, because the two girls who were my best friends were outsiders too:

Everyone else.

My original friendship group - two outsiders and me.

Our friendship became strained as we got older because they became 'normal', whereas I did not, which caused me to feel very lonely:

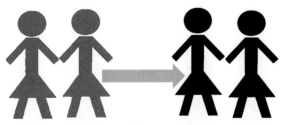

When my friends became 'normal'.

Being an adult means I have far more opportunities to be around people of different ages, interests, jobs and backgrounds. I like **getting to know people on a one to one basis in their own setting** as opposed to knowing people who also all know each other just because we are all together due to the same circumstances such as school and work. None of my current friends know each other. I do different activities with different friends at different times on different days. I think when people are in a group environment they act in a similar manner to each other, even if they do not realise it.

As I have got older, I have developed more confidence in creating opportunities to spend time with people who I have an inkling might be a bit more like me. I would never have had the confidence to do that when I was younger, even if there was someone with whom I felt a slight chance that we might get along.

Summary of what I have learned about being different:

- I accept that I am different but most of the time I do not want to feel that I am
- I feel less different when I am alone or at home
- I feel less different when I am in a group in which members of the group still retain their individuality
- I feel less different when I spend time with people who are also 'outsiders'
- I feel less different when I am with people who are open minded, considerate and good at communicating with me

WHAT i HAVE LEARNED ABOUT MANAGING EMOTIONS

Routine
Alone Time
Staying calm
Who I talk to and about what

Routine

My mood is a bit more stable these days. Let's consider *mood* to be the average of one's feelings at any given time:

In Cognitive Behavioural Therapy (CBT) the formula looks like this:

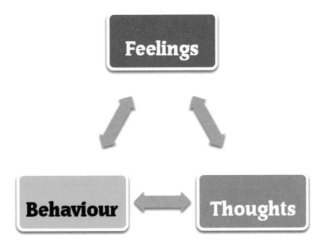

CBT says that the way a person feels, thinks and behaves are all linked to each other. Much has been written about in CBT about how people can change their thoughts to change how they feel. This is a strategy that I use. **I can change my mood by thinking more logically and more optimistically about things.**

However, I find that being able to reduce my mood swings is linked far more to my behaviour. The formula for this part is:

Let's consider *behaviour* to be the activities a person does.

So, if I want to have a more stable mood, I would need to have more stable behaviour… which is what I do. **My day to day activities are the same and they remain consistent,** which means my mood is more consistent. It is important that my **day to day activities are quiet, calm and within my control.** Even doing the same activity will cause massive changes in mood if these are too stimulating. I notice that when I am over stimulated my mood swings are far greater.

When I am doing lots of different things, or doing things that are unstructured or chaotic, my mood is very up and down.

Having a stable life with predictable, planned activities helps create stability. I always try to prepare myself if I know that I am likely to feel a certain way. For example, as I mentioned previously, if I *know* I am going to be socialising, and I *know* that this particular type of socialising is likely to make me feel lonely, I will be able to cope. It will not cause me to have a massive mood swing – because I had *planned* to feel this way.

Unexpected situations can cause me to experience emotion that I did not expect to feel. Unexpected emotions are also likely to be bigger and more difficult to get over. For example, if I have planned to see a friend then I have planned to experience the associated anxiety. I see my friend, I experience the anxiety and then it disappears. If I have not planned to see my friend but I accidentally bump into them anyway the anxiety is much greater and it lingers. If I have planned to hear some bad news then it does not upset me as much as if I had not planned to hear it.

Because my experience of the world and my thought processes are different from most people's, my feelings and reactions to situations can be seen as an overreaction and extreme. My feelings and reactions, however, may well be proportionate to how I experience a situation. People who consider me to be too reactive or extreme have a completely different way of perceiving the world so perhaps that is why they consider my reactions to be out of proportion. A person's perception as to what constitutes an easy or a difficult situation affects how strongly they might react. The misunderstanding comes about because what I perceive to be a large issue would be dismissed by many neurotypicals as nothing to worry about. I consider myself to be a reasonable and logical person but the world appears to be largely unreasonable and illogical to me. In my world I encounter unreasonable and illogical situations all of the time.

Alone Time

I cope with my sensitivity and mood swings by **being on my own** for long periods and minimising my participation in situations that would cause me to feel emotional. I do not watch the news or read newspapers.

Another reason why it is so important for me to have my time alone in the evening (and I turn off my computer and social media in the evening too) is because any social interaction is likely to make me feel further emotion and, if those emotions are strong, then I will not be able to sleep. People saying things to me can make me feel very emotional.

Staying calm

I have learned that I am generally happiest when I feel 'calm'. Calm is defined as: *the absence of strong emotions.*

Being very sensitive and not being able to manage strong emotions very well means that my preference is not to experience strong emotions. When I am calm I feel content and comfortable. When I am experiencing a strong emotion (good or bad) I feel very unsettled and I struggle to focus. My motivation in day to day life is to **find calm, and to maintain that calm feeling,** rather than to go seeking stimulation. Following my routine and getting my boxes ticked makes me feel calm.

Excitement is one of the more difficult emotions to manage. Even though it is a positive emotion, when I feel excited it still makes me unsettled. Since we bought a dog I have been learning a lot about dog training. One idea I came across was that it might not be such a good idea to make your dog excited. An excited dog can feel similar to an anxious dog, or excitement can turn into anxiety. It was an interesting topic and I could relate a lot because when I feel excited it can feel the same as when I feel anxious. So, for certain people in certain situations, excitement might not always be a good thing and might feel similar to anxiety.

I like being excited, but only about a limited number of things at a time, and not all at once, and not at the 'wrong' time because if I feel too excited during, for example, weightlifting or times I ought to be 'off' i.e. when I am recharging, I will not get the most from those situations!

Who I talk to and about what

Another way that I have learned to cope better with my emotional sensitivity and reduce mood swings is to be cautious about who I talk to about myself and my life. Talking to the 'wrong' person can make me feel worse.

I have learned that it is better for me not to say much about myself until I have gained a 'feeling' for those around me and their ability to empathise. The problem with talking to people who are not empathetic is the way they react to the things I say. Their reactions can be extremely hurtful and cause me to have a lingering low mood.

The problem is, because of my ASD, I find it extremely difficult to judge:

1) whether or not someone is empathetic
2) how they are likely to react to the things that I say.

I generally work out point 1 by observing and listening to how they behave and what they say to other people. But even if I can successfully establish that someone is empathetic, I still have major difficulty predicting how they are likely to react to what I say.

Having ASD makes it extremely difficult to predict reactions and consequences. If you are like me, and have no way of knowing what another person thinks or feels, then socialising is a hugely confusing and unsettling thing, as often the things people do and say come as a complete surprise!

I have been very hurt in the past by people who responded to me insensitively, after I was very open with them. I wish I had not said anything to them at all.

When I was at school, I remember there might have been a very small number of occasions when I told my friends about some of my problems, hoping that they would react in a way that made me feel better. For example, in the first term of secondary school everyone had to go away to an activity park for a week. I was terrified by the thought of this and had tantrums at home every single day leading up to it. When I told my friends that I did not want to go, their comments were similar to "Well everyone else is going so you have to as well", "How can you not want to go? It'll be fun!" and "Oh come on, you are always such a loner!"

These comments made me feel awful and had a huge impact on my mood for the rest of the day (and probably the rest of the week, and the time at the activity park). The fact that I still have such a vivid recollection of this situation now, and that it still hurts me, demonstrates very well the impact other people's comments can have. In fact, comments such as these contributed to my mental health problems.

I am very emotionally sensitive. One tiny comment can make me cry or shut down for days. It often feels as though the world has collapsed when something happens that has upset or distressed me even if, logically and intellectually, of course the whole world has not collapsed. I have therefore, learned to be careful about what I say and to whom I say things.

I suspect the sensitivity is largely to do with impaired theory of mind and having difficulty seeing the bigger picture and predicting outcomes or responses to situations. Sometimes, if I do or say something, I feel completely in the dark and have no idea what the consequence will be.

Often I am quiet because I cannot 'read' people. Whenever I say something, I risk that another person's reaction will make me feel an upsetting emotion I have not prepared for.

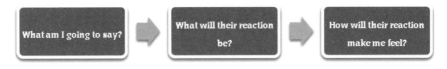

It takes time for me to trust someone. If I speak to someone, it is because I trust that their reply is not going to upset me, otherwise I am very quiet.

For example, if I want to tell someone about a piece of my work that I am very proud of, and would like to talk about it in detail, but their response is very short and brief, I will feel upset instead of happy and proud, which is not the way I wanted to feel. I will then spend a long, long time wondering why they reacted like this and feeling upset about it.

My mood goes from happy and proud to deflated. There was no positive emotional benefit to me from telling them. I learned that, maybe, I should not have told them anything in order to protect my own feelings.

Similarly, I have learned that there is no point me telling certain people about my weightlifting (even if I like the people and they like me) because I know they are not as interested in it as much as I am or because they do not know as much detail as I feel is necessary to truly appreciate what I say. They probably will not take as much interest or show as much excitement in it as I would wish for. This would end up making me feel disappointed. My mood would go from happy to being upset. I choose to be quiet about this topic rather than risk feeling upset by a response I consider insufficient.

A strategy that I have learned to cope with life generally is to be able to **predict how situations are going to be and this also includes how situations are going to make me feel.** Just as I like to know what I am going to be doing, I like to know how that situation is likely going to make me feel. Unfortunately, conversations are hard to prepare for. It is very hard to predict what emotions are going to be felt during a conversation, merely because by nature, conversations are unpredictable.

If I am to tell someone something, I consider the following:

I work out whether or not someone has a naturally empathetic personality. This is the first step. If they are, it is a strong indicator that they will be a good person to talk to. If they are not, I will probably never be open with them. Sometimes I deliberately do not tell the people I know about things that are important to me because I know they will react to me in the 'wrong' way.

I build up trust with someone. If I say something to them it is because I trust them, otherwise I am very quiet.

I talk to people who I am familiar with. I am more able to predict and imagine how someone is going to react if it is someone I am familiar with. Familiarity means I might be a bit more open with them because, if we have a good relationship, I will feel more comfortable preparing for, and responding to, their reactions to the things I say. With people I know well, even if something they say unsettles me, it is easier to tell them that they have and explain why.

I have learned that it helps to **learn about an individual; what they** are interested in; and the way they respond to the things I tell them. I can create a 'database' in my head that tells me, for example, that Friend A might not respond in the 'right' way if I tell her about how my weightlifting is going, but if I tell her about my cats and dog her responses make me feel very good. I therefore learn to talk more to her about my animals and less to her about my weightlifting. A positive consequence of this is that I end up having situation-specific relationships, i.e. **I talk about and do specific things with specific people** (which is a strategy I use to have successful relationships).

If you are autistic, it may help you to make your own table or flowchart with information about subjects you wish to talk about and the people you know, and work out who is appropriate to talk to about each subject.

Summary of what I have learned about managing emotions:

My mood is dependent on my behaviour (the activities I do day to day). Therefore, it is important that I aim to:

- Stay within my comfort zone and only do those activities that fit my comfort zone
- Carry out more or less the same things every day
- Stick to my daily or weekly routine
- Have plenty of Alone Time

I am very emotionally sensitive so it is important for me to aim to feel 'calm' rather than any other emotion. I am careful about who I talk to. I can experience some very positive feelings when I talk about the right things to the right people but some very negative feelings if I talk to the wrong people or talk to people about the wrong things.

WHAT i HAVE LEARNED ABOUT EMPATHY

What is empathy?
The three levels

What is empathy?

I have learned that being empathetic is the absolute foundation to any successful relationship. I want people to be empathetic towards me and **I am continually trying to be empathetic** towards other people. I am *not* naturally an empathetic person.

There are various definitions of empathy and people seem to think about it in all sorts of ways. I consider empathy to be: *feeling what another person is feeling.* A simple example of empathy in action is being at your school's football match and when your team scores everyone in the crowd stands up and cheers. They are all feeling the exact same feeling at the same time:

I know that a lot of autistic people feel strongly about the subject of empathy and disagree with the stereotypical perception that autistic people lack empathy.

My own views are that:

1) many people get being 'empathetic' confused with being 'emotional'. Here is an example using 'excitement' as the emotion:

On her own, the girl with the curly hair is emotional...

With her friend together, they are both excited. She is empathetic.

2) some autistic people have lots of empathy, some have very little, and many are in between

3) empathy varies according to the particular situation. It is not a static measure (see football cartoon on previous page. If it were me in the crowd, I would be feeling very overwhelmed and wanting to leave!)

4) autistic people are likely to lack empathy *if we remember that* empathy requires putting yourself in another person's shoes. Putting yourself in another person's shoes requires quite a sophisticated level of social ability.

Different views

Two people having a different view about a particular situation can lead to a lack of empathy on both sides. Autistic and neurotypical people are likely to both have a different view. So for example, if I cannot relate to my neurotypical friend's enjoyment when they go on holiday (because going on holiday would be very stressful for me), then unless I am able to put myself in their shoes, I cannot have empathy for them. Similarly, if someone cannot relate to my enjoyment of weightlifting (because they hate exercise!), unless they are able to put themselves in my shoes, they cannot have empathy for me. As you can see, being able to put yourself in another person's shoes is an incredibly important part of being an empathetic person, but I personally find that extremely hard to do due to my ASD.

This year I have submitted the films that I have produced to some film festivals. The thought of attending any film festival fills me with anxiety and makes me stressed. However, if I tell someone about a film festival I am considering visiting to see my film shown (either before or after the showing), they tend to get very excited and want to hear more. This is typically the last way I want someone to react because going to the film festival, although exciting and important, causes me a lot of stress. Hearing that a person gets so excited over something that makes me feel stressed can make me feel isolated.

Going to a film festival is stressful because doing something like this exposes all of my difficulties (coping with change in routine, travelling, getting organised, planning, busy, overwhelming environments and social networking...) and is a challenge to my introverted, quiet type of personality. So, to hear and feel people show excitement for me is understandable... because it is exciting... *but* I would also like them to first and foremost appreciate just how excruciatingly difficult something like that is for me. Most people do not have the challenges I do, so unless they understand me and my autism, they would not intuitively understand how I feel. **It is my responsibility to tell people about my challenges** and their responsibility to take the time to listen, understand and be compassionate.

Lots of very normal things are very stressful and difficult for me (the film festival is written as an 'extreme' only for the purpose of giving an example), which makes it hard to talk about many of the things I do. I think people could be interested in the things I do but are sometimes limited because they are thinking about how those things would be if *they* did them rather than how those things are for *me*. Having the ability to put yourself in another person's shoes is a very important part of building any relationship but so many people do not do it.

Perhaps my conclusion is that **I only really want to talk to people about my life and the things that I do when I trust that whoever I** am speaking to is someone who is understanding and empathetic towards my autism.

Telling people what I do usually shows them *what is on the outside* rather than what goes on the inside (they see my achievements and activities rather than my thoughts and feelings). This is a large problem I have had throughout my life. People *see* the things I achieve without recognising the stress, anxiety and effort that they have taken. It is one of the reasons why I have found it so hard to feel connected to anyone.

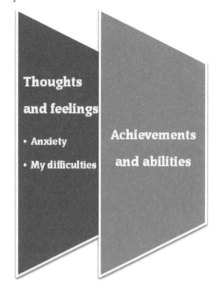

Should I happen to mention that I will be attending a film festival and someone says to me in response "That is so exciting!" or even worse "You must be so excited!" I may end up feeling even more anxious. It is definitely exciting but the primary feeling I have is anxiety. I would rather someone say "That is so exciting but I understand that you must be feeling anxious too" or "I understand that going to the film festival will be very, very hard for you". Otherwise I feel disconnected because their response just reminds me that I am different.

I very much appreciate the people I have in my life who are empathetic!

Sometimes I do not want to talk to anyone because I suspect that the response I get back will not be empathetic and that they will not understand my point of view or, even worse, I feel that they do not *want* to understand my point of view. For example, if I try to explain to someone that attending a film festival for the screening of my film is exciting – but more accurately it is very stressful and hard – and they respond by dismissing what I have said and continue talking about the film festival being exciting, I struggle to see the point of talking to them at all.

I have two examples of this:

Example: weightlifting coach

I had one weightlifting coach who kept pestering me to take part in weightlifting competitions. He encouraged me to compete, despite me very clearly telling him that I was not interested. It was irritating and stressful and made me lose interest in my coaching sessions.

Example: A level teachers

Certain A level teachers kept encouraging me to apply for prestigious (but distant) universities. "You should be applying for [this university]" and "Why on earth are you applying for that one?" were not empathetic comments. Had they truly considered *my* personality and *my* position in life, they would have understood exactly why I went to the university I did, and they probably would have agreed it was the right decision for *me,* especially as I had told them that I wanted to go there because it was near my home.

My teachers did not know I had ASD, though my lifting coach did, although they all knew me well enough to know my personality. However, those teachers and the weightlifting coach were not able to put themselves in my shoes, despite knowing me and knowing the reasons for my decisions. Receiving comments like the ones they made not only made me feel isolated, they also filled me with self-doubt and made me question my own instinctive judgment and decisions. As I have already mentioned, a big contributor to my mental health problems is being pushed into things that, intrinsically I know are not right for me. I have always known what is the best route for me to be following, but having other people suggest otherwise, is unsettling and sets me off track. For example, I always knew that I needed a large amount of Alone Time. Alone Time is what makes me happy and what makes me function. Other people suggesting that I ought not be having so much time alone or, even worse, taking me away from my Alone Time, ultimately led to the deterioration of my mental health.

When you have people around you telling you that you are probably doing the wrong thing, you start to doubt yourself. I always say that, when I am alone and it is just me and my judgment, decisions are always very clear. I have a fairly strong sense of self and what I like and do not like. It is only when other people bring in their opinion and perspective that mine becomes confused and distorted. Those decisions become less clear. It is important to hear and see a different perspective but it should be neutral and not judgemental or pushy, and the person giving their perspective should always remember that *they are not you.* They ought to be clear when advising – are they advising based on their own circumstances, or yours?

The three levels

I think that relating to someone can be done on three different levels, empathy being the deepest one. The three levels I believe exist are:

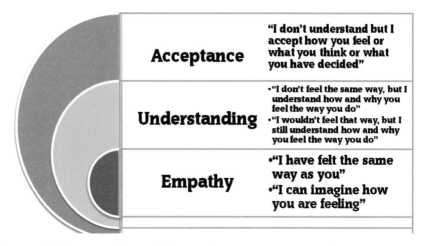

	Acceptance	"I don't understand but I accept how you feel or what you think or what you have decided"
	Understanding	• "I don't feel the same way, but I understand how and why you feel the way you do" • "I wouldn't feel that way, but I still understand how and why you feel the way you do"
	Empathy	• "I have felt the same way as you" • "I can imagine how you are feeling"

The weightlifting coach could not relate to me on any of these levels. I was very brave and forthright from the beginning, stating that *I did not want* to compete in weightlifting because it would make me too anxious and weightlifting would no longer be enjoyable.

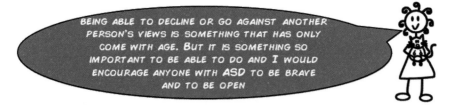

BEING ABLE TO DECLINE OR GO AGAINST ANOTHER PERSON'S VIEWS IS SOMETHING THAT HAS ONLY COME WITH AGE. BUT IT IS SOMETHING SO IMPORTANT TO BE ABLE TO DO AND I WOULD ENCOURAGE ANYONE WITH ASD TO BE BRAVE AND TO BE OPEN

Even if the coach just did the very minimum and 'accepted' that I was not going to be competing, would have helped. Some people will not bother with trying to understand or will not be able to be empathetic, but everyone can learn to do the basics and accept the way a person is. I found another coach, who was accepting, understanding and empathetic towards me for me and my choice not to compete.

Since I know how awful it makes me feel when other people do not put themselves in my shoes, **I have learned the importance of putting myself in other people's shoes.** When I talk to people I do not make any assumptions about how they experience the world. If they tell me something they did for example, my first thought is usually "I wonder how that was for them" or, if I know them well, I might be able to work out for myself how it was for them and can then give an empathetic response. For example, if I have a friend who enjoys socialising and went out with friends at the weekend I can confidently say "That must have been lovely for you". If it is someone I do not know I will be more likely to say "Did you have a good time? Do you like that sort of thing?" **I do not like to assume how another person experiences the world.**

Example of giving an empathetic response.

If I have a friend who has ASD or is introverted and tells me that they did something different or amazing I can say with confidence "That must have been difficult" because - even though it was different and amazing - I have empathy for them because, I know myself, the effort they must have made to do it and the stress it caused them making that effort.

I have a friend who also does weightlifting and she has started competing recently. Although I do not relate to her enjoyment of it (the idea of competing fills me with dread!), I still understand and support her because I know that *she* likes it.

Summary of what I have learned about empathy:

- Do not make assumptions about how people think and feel
- It is important not to assume that all people see things in the same way as you do
- It is important to put yourself in someone else's shoes which means thinking about a situation *as though you were them* in that situation, *not* as though it was you in their situation
- Find out about a person's personality, strengths and difficulties. Then put yourself in their shoes when they tell you about something they have done

WHAT i HAVE LEARNED ABOUT WORKiNG

Full time and part time employment
Self-employment
Entrepreneurship

I have had a few different jobs each with different ways of working:
* I have been in full time employment
* I have been in part time employment
* I have been self employed
* I have run my own business

Full time and part time employment

My single experience of being in full time employment taught me that it was not what I wanted to do! The *work* was fine. I was a project manager in a laboratory and the work included writing reports and analysing test results. These were tasks that interested me, so I quite liked the work. The office was small with only 4 other people in it. I would say that all but one were introverted so I did not have to say much and nobody spoke much to me.

The hours were flexible so that I could start work at 8am and leave at 4pm. I am a morning person and, as we know, I like to get things done sooner in the day, so it was important to me that work was completed as soon as possible so that I could get home, have time to do my hobbies, be alone and recharge. I have done shifts before where I started at 2pm and I remember feeling tense the whole day up until that time, doing very little, being unproductive and feeling very agitated.

I soon learned that the biggest problem with full time employment is that, just like school, it takes up such an enormous proportion of the day that there is not any time left for my own hobbies and projects, nor for recharging.

The job was local to me so I used to walk to the office through the park. It was helpful that **I could be active in the morning.** Being active first thing generally makes me feel much better. I used to lift weights as often as I could before or after work and I still did my newspaper round. However, throughout my time at that job, I had no life and energy for anything other than the job. Everything else suffered including my weightlifting, hobbies, sleep and relationships. By the time I got home I was so exhausted that I could not really concentrate, nor did I have any desire to do anything else. It was a very similar experience to when I was at school. The difference, at least, was that I was not being bullied and that I was earning money!

Before I learned about autism, it used to astound me how much energy people seemed to have. I have always been very aware of myself in comparison with other people and I could see that people were still up for doing fun or social activities after school, after work or at weekends. People used to invite me to join in but I invariably declined. I always felt exhausted. I wondered how people were able to achieve this work-life balance. I also wondered if this is what life was going to be like forever? Was I going to have to work-sleep-work, constantly feeling exhausted with no energy or motivation to do anything else... forever? It was a daunting and thoroughly depressing vision.

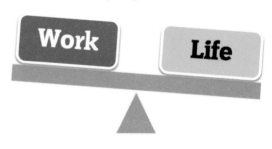

The Work-Life balance is something I take very seriously.

Work	School or University or Job – anything that consumes the majority of one's time

I understand that most neurotypical people can achieve a reasonable work-life balance. I think that *I* find (and some autistic people find) getting the right balance much more difficult. When I am working, and when I am in education, the amount of energy I use means I am too stressed, overwhelmed and exhausted to have a fulfilling life outside of these times. It also explains why I rarely spend time with the few friends I have whenever I am working. Many fledging relationships have failed because I was always too tired to see anyone.

I have also been employed part time where I worked between 3 and 5 hours a day in an office. I learned that **the fewer hours spent outside of my home the better.** Working shorter hours meant a much more comfortable life in terms of me feeling slightly less tired. I still also felt enormously restricted by the boundaries of employment. To say that being employed is soul destroying is really the perfect description. I am too much of a free spirit and my special needs mean that I cannot successfully maintain that sort of lifestyle.

I also have had problems handling change in the workplace. I remember once my old manager wanted to give me a promotion but I was happy doing what I was doing, so I did not accept. I actually ended up leaving that job as the pressure to do more was too much. I was just happy as things were.

I have also noticed that, in the places I have worked, many of the people come across as being quite similar. I have read newspaper articles and literature online that states that employers just find it easier to employ people who are alike. This can cause me to feel very different and lonely, which is another deterrent to working in this traditional way.

There were possibly two ways for me to have a better experience of working:

- Become self-employed and ideally work mostly from home
- Do Work that is such an integral part of me that it becomes part of Life as well

This is what I have done and this is how I have been able to cope with working.

I find it very, very uncomfortable working in a shared space and being around when other people are talking. The result is sensory overload. Talking is distracting, both because of noise and what is being talked about (annoying for me if it is non-work related). Sensory overload also includes sound and the smell of food (B.A.N.A.N.A.s[7]), fragrances and anything else that one might find in an office environment. These make me feel nauseous and then it is hard to concentrate on my work. An office environment has a lot of other distractions with people coming and going, doors opening and closing and the general background humdrum

7 I dislike them so much and I dislike the word too!

of office life.

People stopping by, or coming up to me and spontaneously talking when I am working, is not easy to cope with because this is a type of transition. If I have not planned to have a conversation it is really hard for me to suddenly have one and to have to stop what I am working on. My strategies to deal with interruptions were always to say to people, "I'm sorry, I'm a bit busy right now. Could you come back in [10 minutes]?" Alternatively, I would always encourage people to email me instead. It helped a bit but it still meant my hyperfocus got broken. I would never feel that I achieved what I wanted, nor to the standard, that I had set myself.

I am good at managing having many tasks to do **as long as I get each task done and as long as external distractions are kept to a minimum. Completing tasks** is an important factor for me. Tasks that take a long time or that require constant stopping and starting, or that I never get to see through from start to end, cause me stress. This is the reason **I prefer to work under my own direction.**

Being able to complete tasks and tick boxes is important. It is much easier to complete tasks if I am working for myself. I am not the sort of person who can start my working day: 1) not knowing what I am going to be doing, and 2) not knowing for certain that I am going to get at least one thing finished. I find tasks that are ambiguous or that have no definite end difficult. Being able to tick a box is one of the greatest ways to self-motivate. **I like to remind myself during the night what boxes I managed to tick** that day.

The inability to complete tasks, such as my manager constantly moving me on to something else (regardless of whether the current task is complete), tasks being too reliant on other people so causing delays, and tasks that are not really clear from the outset, mean that working for, and with, other people is very challenging. When I work for myself **I always make sure there is a clear end to a task and that I have enough time to finish.**

Generally, I maintain a life of autonomy and aim to be as independent as I can. **I like to work independently.** Other people's actions which affect my work can be very frustrating. I am very reliable, very organised and very efficient. Working with people who are not like this is not easy. Here is an example:

Magazine deadline example

There is a deadline for an article I have written to be published in a magazine on Friday. I requested the relevant photos to go with the article from my colleague two weeks ago. Despite chasing up I have still not received them. To miss a deadline for an article that I have spent a lot of time working on, in order to establish a publication deal with a magazine, makes me feel extremely unhappy.

I always prefer to work alone and to take responsibility for as much of the work as possible. This is another thing that helps me to be a good entrepreneur!

I find it hard to multi-task when other people expect me to. If I am working on something and *my* mind decides that I need to do something else, my mind has already made a mental transition and it is easy to shift to the other task. I have been able to figure out in my head exactly what I am going to do and how, and the way all the other tasks are going to be affected. If somebody *else* tells me to spontaneously do something else: 1) it breaks my hyperfocus, and 2) my mind does not have a chance to make the mental transition. Because I do not have the flexible thinking skills I cannot work out, on the spot, how to re-prioritise and re-schedule all the tasks that I am doing.

I always prefer advance notice and to have a planned time for tasks. For example, my manager coming up to me and saying "I need you to work on this now instead" used to be very stressful – but had he emailed me <Please could you plan to work on [this] [this afternoon]?> would have been fine.

Slower paced jobs suit me a lot more because I am less likely to be distracted and can work on one task at a time.

Generally being unable to become, and remain, hyperfocussed is something I find really hard about working. There are always too many distractions at work!

I also prefer jobs where I am managed as little as possible because:

1) I am distracted much less
2) interacting makes me anxious
3) my natural self is self-motivated, intuitive, responsible and reliable.

Being managed can disturb my own ways of working.

My executive function impairments have led me to always figure out how to do things efficiently… so often I do things more efficiently than someone else, or more efficiently than the way someone else might tell me to do it. **I like working with people who do not care about how something is done, they just care about the end result.**

These are all things I have learned in my working life. These strategies and snippets of insight are also relevant to other aspects of my life.

Self-employment

At the time of writing, I have various forms of Work, which are:

- Entrepreneur and Founder of The Curly Hair Project, a social enterprise that supports people on the autistic spectrum and the people around them
- Marketer for veterinary businesses
- I also do my newspaper round and on occasion ad-hoc activities like freelance writing and dog walking

Working from home is really the only way I am able to maintain a successful working life. I think that I *could* manage being employed *if* I was able to work from home, with some **flexibility in terms of hours and times of work.** However, I know that I would be unfulfilled emotionally.

Being self-employed is the ideal way for me to work. I have control over what projects I undertake as well as how and when I work on them. Another benefit for me of being self-employed is that I am able to control the amount of interaction with my clients.

My anxieties and difficulties with social interactions have forced me to become quite self-sufficient and independent in the vast majority of things I undertake. I do so much that might typically be delegated between 3 or 4 separate people. Most people who know me wonder how I can do so much high quality work! The possible answers to this are that:

1) I *have* to be this way because interacting with people is so difficult, and 2) because I only trust myself to do the work to the required standard! To my managers and clients I am reliable, trustworthy and I do a good job.

Working for myself gives me flexibility and control in what and when I do something. If I am not in the mood to do a particular task then I will leave it for that moment and do something else instead, until I am ready to do the original task. I can take lots of breaks, move around, stroke my animals, text and call my family and friends, eat and drink when I want and go out at any time. Most importantly, I can get my Hyperfocus Time when I need it!

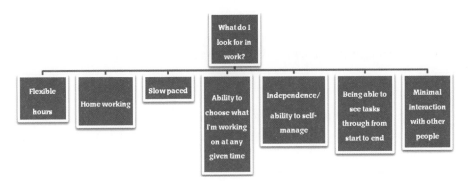

I have had to accept that it is incredibly difficult for me to work in any workplace environment other than my own. The longest time I was in full time employment was thirteen months. Looking back and understanding my ASD now (and I had not been diagnosed at the time), I think I did amazingly well to cope for so long!

Choosing which university to go to was a very easy choice for me as it just had to be the nearest one. I needed to stay at home as much as possible, and to get to and from home as quickly as possible, including during free periods of the day, in order to have some Alone Time.

Looking back over my life, it makes me aware of just how much physical and emotional discomfort I put myself through, just because the things I was doing were things I thought I should be doing. I thought I was oversensitive and needed to toughen up, or simply "learn to cope with life better". To know now that I *do* have challenges that most other people do *not* have has given me a new perspective on life and I am kinder to myself. I understand that I have choices and can make adjustments for myself. Working can be really difficult but I now have a fulfilling career because I have adapted life to suit me.

I do not think I could go back to university, or work in a public environment ever again. If I did, I believe I would simply revert to having depressed feelings and suffer from exhaustion. Therefore, it is not an option that I would consider at this current stage of my life. Instead I have workarounds for my problems and I am making my living and building my independence in other ways.

I have never actually had any idea about what I wanted to do as a career nor had any aspirations at all. Some of the reasons are because I have always worried about the: 1) tiredness and not being able to recharge, and, 2) lack of Alone Time and freedom that any job would be able to offer. There are limitations to the jobs and careers I could have because it is difficult for me to be around people for too long and be out of my house for too long. I am very fortunate to have created the current working arrangements that I have.

Entrepreneurship

Education and studying has never come naturally to me. To look at my exam results and my degree on paper would suggest that I am bright and academic. The irony is that I do not feel that way and I massively prefer other activities to studying.

Whenever I am in a group situation and learning something new (regardless of whether it is academic, practical, fun or serious) I am usually the last person to understand the point - if I get the point at all! My friend and I had some tennis lessons some years ago, given by a coach. Over the six lessons my friend became really good and was very responsive to the coaching, whereas I did not improve at all. In fact, I got the sense that the coach did not really know what to do with me!

I remember an interview I had for the position of Laboratory Chemist. Despite having always done well in my assignments and coming out with a first class chemistry degree and achieving a Masters at university, I was not able to answer the theoretical chemistry based questions at the interview.

I used to think of myself as someone who was academic but I think it is more that I *present* that way because of my educational achievements rather than who I actually am. Instead, I consider myself to be an extremely hard worker, very disciplined, with a lot of self-motivation as opposed to being academic.

I think I have a different way of thinking, which makes me innovative. I think all these traits are why I am so entrepreneurial and have ended up doing what I am doing. Professionals in business have often remarked to me: "I have met many people like you who are true entrepreneurs and all they do is work, work, and work all the time". They are right. Even if I was very rich or even if I was retired, I know that I would still work all the time.

When I was at school I used to spend all my free time during weekends and evenings catching up on what we had learned during lessons. I remember a family friend commenting every time she came over, "You're always working, Alis!" or "You work so hard!" I had to! Otherwise I would not have passed my exams. I did not learn effectively during school so I had no other choice than to teach myself outside of school.

Years later, I have not changed. I have built my businesses from scratch. Everything I have done and continue to do has been self-taught and I have worked things out along the way.

I am really proud of The Curly Hair Project. It has not only helped me understand myself a lot better, it has helped thousands of other people too. Getting feedback that says that my work has changed someone's life is just the most rewarding and wonderful feeling. I have found a working arrangement that I can not only maintain but that I can excel at. I am fortunate but I am also very hard working, innovative and intuitive.

The differentiation between work and life outside work is not so important to me anymore, because my work energises me and is emotionally fulfilling. My life is very much centered around three things: weightlifting, my pets and working. If I wanted, I would be able to do other things (which I do not, as I am content with a life like this) because my work is energising rather than draining.

Weightlifting is one of the most important parts of my day. I am so glad that I have enough energy to truly devote myself to it. **Being able to fit my life around weightlifting** rather than the other way round has really helped my mental well-being. My suggestion to autistic individuals is to **prioritise your special interest** in day to day life.

Other advice for people on the autistic spectrum would be to take a lot of care to **create a good work-life balance.** Ideally, you want to ensure that work is energising or at least does not consume so much of your energy that there is nothing left for anything else. Working from home, running your own business, doing work that involves your special interest, working remotely, working part time, working near to home may be ways in which energy depletion is minimised. The ideal solution of course, may merely be to do something that you really, really enjoy!

Summary of what I have learned about working:

- The most important thing is the Work-Life balance which is easier to achieve through self-employment
- Flexible working is very important
- Doing something that you really love is important

WHAT i HAVE LEARNED ABOUT PRODUCTiViTY

Information processing
Working style

Information processing

I have learned that the way information is communicated is really important. Everybody has a natural preference as to the way they work and learn best but generally most neurotypical people seem to have similar preferences. Since the world is mostly populated with neurotypicals it makes sense that most information is communicated in a neurotypical-friendly way. I suspect that the reason why most lessons or lectures take place in a classroom with one teacher speaking at the front, occasionally using a whiteboard, with all students sitting next to one another, listening and writing is because this is an effective way of teaching for most of the students.

Similarly, I suspect that the reason most organisations have offices where people come in to work is because that is how work gets done most effectively. I once asked an old manager whether I could work from home instead of working in the office and his response was, "I am not keen on that idea. I like people to be together sharing ideas and talking". That might well be effective for the organisation as a whole and for members of the team, but that way was so stressful and unsuitable for me that it actually limited how well I could work. A few weeks later I left that job. Even though I was really good at it, I could not cope with the environment.

If I need to be shown how to do something, **the person must use very, very clear language and not miss out any steps** (steps that other people would consider obvious). An example of this is that only a few days ago my dad asked me to hold a piece of perspex up against the window whilst he fitted it. He explained what to do whilst he showed me, but I still felt

159

confused. I did not know exactly what he meant and where exactly I should be holding the perspex. Then he started getting cross with me for not being able to understand. It was a frustrating scenario for me and for him. I was getting confused because I felt that he was not explaining well and I had started to feel stupid which is not good for my self-esteem.

Working out how to do things is very, very hard. It is therefore **best for me to be left alone to figure out how to do something in my own way,** at my own pace - then I do not frustrate anybody and I do not feel completely bewildered! This strategy is also what makes me a good entrepreneur!

Something that the people I have worked for liked about me is that they can rely on me to do what they need without having to teach me, regardless of whether or not I have done the task before. They know they can rely on me to find out. I do not take up much of their time because my preferred way of learning is to work something out for myself. I will be more likely to remember and I will not have to deal with the anxiety that comes from the interaction (which slows down and hinders the learning process as well). Unless a person thinks and sees things in the same way as me, or is a good communicator and can adapt their way of teaching to suit my thinking style, it is better for me to learn how to do things on my own.

Perhaps it was the general environment of school and university that made learning hard for me, but, in truth, no particular teacher stands out as someone who made me love learning and want to understand a subject.

Working style

I do not have any one particular working style. I know that:

- I am interested in facts and reason
- I do not learn from listening to people
- I prefer visuals and graphs
- I like to read
- I like to try things for myself
- I need to take my time and I need a particular environment free of interruption
- I have an awful short term memory and that includes anything that I might read or anything people might say to me
- I have a short attention span and need concise and to-the-point information

I think there are many aspects of learning and working that are important to consider. I have illustrated these in the following diagram:

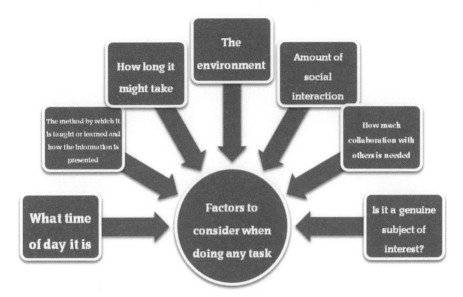

The *method* by which something is carried out is just *one* factor. For example, I might be watching a video tutorial on how to do a particular weightlifting exercise (watching a short, to-the-point video is generally a good way for me to learn weightlifting technique), but if the room is noisy or disruptive, or if it is late in the day when I am tired, I probably will not absorb very much.

Being self-employed and running my own businesses have enabled me to have control over all these factors and I am probably more productive now than I have ever been!

I have had a couple of Olympic weightlifting coaches. Olympic weightlifting is a very technical and complicated sport. I am fairly proficient at it now, largely because I have been able to learn it in my own way. For example, the time that I do weightlifting is very important. Since I have generally always been able to **do weightlifting at the time that suits me,** it has really helped me learn the techniques. I did not learn as well when I had sessions with my coach at times that were not optimal for me.

The environment is very important as well of course, so **I do my weightlifting in my garage** at home so that I have control of the setup. One coach wanted me to go and have lessons in his busy gym instead. There would have been too many factors outside of my control and outside of my preferences for me to have been able to do weightlifting to the best of my ability.

Duration is another interesting aspect to consider. Some activities are too long in duration for my participation to be effective whilst other activities are too short. For example, I needed an hour to learn how to use an item of equipment in the laboratory where I worked during my job whereas it was anticipated that I would only need 10 minutes!

To put an autistic person on to a task alongside those who are neurotypical is probably not the best way of allowing someone with ASD to flourish.

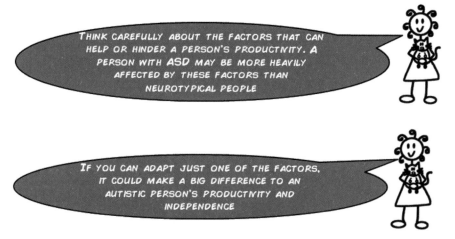

THINK CAREFULLY ABOUT THE FACTORS THAT CAN HELP OR HINDER A PERSON'S PRODUCTIVITY. A PERSON WITH ASD MAY BE MORE HEAVILY AFFECTED BY THESE FACTORS THAN NEUROTYPICAL PEOPLE

IF YOU CAN ADAPT JUST ONE OF THE FACTORS, IT COULD MAKE A BIG DIFFERENCE TO AN AUTISTIC PERSON'S PRODUCTIVITY AND INDEPENDENCE

One of my favourite quotes is "I do not have common sense because I am uncommon" (it means there are fewer autistic people than neurotypicals in the world). The world runs in a very neurotypical-orientated way, but autistic thought processes, strengths and weaknesses are different from neurotypicals'. I do things in ways that are easier, simpler, or quicker for me - which might seem different to the way in which most people do things:

However, if a neurotypical person was able to put themselves in my shoes they would agree that the way I do things is the right and best way for me:

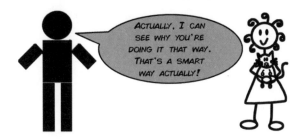

This goes back to the point I make about people lacking empathy for those who are different. The concept of 'putting yourself in my shoes' is usually understood as 'to put myself in your position' but it is perhaps far more important 'to put myself in your position *as though I were you*'. Both of these abilities are helpful because you get to see things from a different perspective, but being able to truly connect with someone on a deep level will require the ability 'to put myself in your position as though I were you'.

So, if somebody sees me doing something that they feel is unusual or seems very complicated and subsequently become judgemental, or even tells me to do it another way, it could be because they are thinking about doing it as though they were them. Of course it would be strange or complicated if *they* were doing it. But it is not them doing it! I see many people doing things that look complicated or seem inefficient to me, but I accept that that is just how they do things and that it works for them.

Summary of what I have learned about productivity:

- Productivity is dependent on a number of factors which may have a greater, more significant effect (good or bad) on autistic people than neurotypical people
- Improving just one of these factors can make a massive difference to an autistic person's productivity
- Autistic people may do things in slightly different ways, but this does not mean their ways are 'wrong' (in fact, often these ways are the most effective ways for *them!*)

WHAT i HAVE LEARNED ABOUT EXECUTIVE FUNCTION

What is executive function?
Transitions
Sensory processing

What is executive function?

Executive function is defined as *the set of mental skills that help people get things done.* Executive function includes skills that directly relate to tasks: remembering things, being able to plan and prioritise, organising, estimating how long it takes to do certain things, keeping to time, not getting distracted, starting tasks and switching between tasks.

Since being diagnosed, although I had heard of the term, I had not really thought much about executive function because, funnily enough, I did not think it was something that overly affected me. In many books I had read, I skipped past these chapters! I have achieved so many things in my life and I have such excellent academic results that I

wondered how could executive function really affect me? How wrong I was! My view was very uninformed!

Since learning more about executive function, and about ASD generally, I have realised that just because I have achieved things it does not mean that: 1) they were not all really hard, and 2) I managed to do them without support, assistance and workarounds. The more I think about my life, the more difficulties I now realise have stood in my path. Somehow, maybe intuitively, and maybe because my family are really supportive, I have made adaptations that have enabled me to do all the things I do, and do them well.

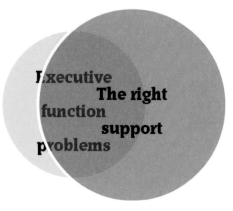

Maybe having the correct support has masked the severity of my executive function problems.

Something else I discovered when learning about executive function is that it also refers to the skills of *self control, emotional regulation and flexible thinking.* I definitely have a problem in all of these areas but I did not always realise that these were a part of executive function.

When I reflect on how I experience daily life I can see that everything I do takes a large amount of thinking, analysing, checking, double checking and remembering. The way I experience life is very much a long list of conscious thoughts, checking in with how I am feeling, what I am doing, what do I need to do and what do I need to say. I did not always realise that it was not this way for everyone. Learning about autism has taught me that neurotypical people do not have such extreme or conscious thoughts continually taking place. They do many things automatically. There is at least one benefit of having such conscious thinking though. This is similar to the recommended technique of Mindfulness which encourages regular breaks during the day to 'check in' with yourself by consciously considering whether what you are doing is matching your daily goal. I do this all the time anyway. I am very aware of what I am doing *all the time.*

I like to illustrate it like this. Imagine this diagram[8] is a neurotypical brain. It shows that there is bigger capacity for 'unaware thinking' and a smaller capacity for 'aware thinking':

8 Alis Rowe (2018). Asperger's Syndrome and Executive Function. London: Lonely Mind Books. 16-19

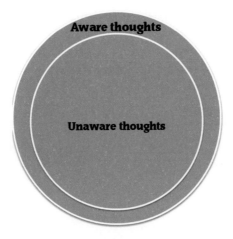

But to me, it feels like my (ASD) brain is more like this:

It feels like I have *more* thoughts that I am aware of, or perhaps more *capacity* for awareness-type thinking. Neurotypicals can do 'normal' tasks without much thought and these tasks are processed in the unaware thinking part of the brain; things like sensory processing, emotional regulation, social interactions and theory of mind also happen quite automatically for neurotypical people.

I have noticed a positive trend. **When I am doing 'normal' things, for example staying within my routine, I am very, very organised and very, very reliable.** Executive function problems tend to occur when I am doing things that are different or new. This had led me to conclude that **my desire for sameness and need to stay inside my routine is my natural way of minimising my executive function difficulties and making my life easier.**

When I am out, when I am doing something different, or when someone else makes a change that affects me, or when someone else is in control of the plan for the day, a lot more mental effort is used in order to keep up. This means there is far less mental energy available to use on the task in hand. Here is an example:

Paperwork and meeting example

I had a meeting and had to take some paperwork with me. The email instructions stated that: "without the paperwork the meeting would not take place".

I left finding this paperwork to the last minute (because I live in the moment!). Unfortunately the paperwork was more difficult to find than I had anticipated. I could not find it. I then thought I would have to cancel the meeting. I then worked out that I would be able to find what I needed on the internet and that I would able to take printed copies, so I printed out the papers and left them in a safe place whilst I got ready. I left my house and turned up at the meeting place. The Receptionist asked me for the paperwork. I looked in my bag; I did not have the papers! After all that I had left it behind!

I also spent so much effort getting ready for the meeting that concentrating on the meeting was really tiring (they fortunately did allow the meeting to proceed and simply asked for me to email the paperwork over later!).

So another reason for the importance of having a routine is because it reduces the effort required for managing executive function. If I am doing the same thing every time, the mental energy I expend is very small!

People often think that I am rigid about times and plans because I am anxious (or just because they think I am indeed very "rigid"!!!) but the other major reason for being rigid is because it solves so many of my executive function issues. I rely on my **carefully organised routines** to be productive and successful.

People might well tease me for being so rigid and meticulous but..

....these same people also remark on how reliable, productive, efficient and organised I am.

People who do not have executive function impairments may find it difficult to appreciate how much brain activity is going on each and every time they do anything. They are just not really aware of it.

Since understanding my ASD I have a lot more respect and admiration for myself and how resilient and how well I did when life was not as quiet, minimalist, peaceful, solitary and routine-structured as it is now. My executive function impairments have contributed to some really, really stressful experiences, but I just thought I was not as clever or as organised as everyone else. So I was always just working very hard to try to keep up with everyone else, not knowing that the difficulties I was having were down to problems with executive function.

Executive function impairments explains why as a child:

*   I had to check, double and triple check that I had the right books with me to take to school every single morning (as well as having to check the night before!)
*   I had to write such long, thorough instructions in my homework diary whereas most people just seemed to remember
*   It took me so many more hours than everyone else to revise for tests
*   I found it excruciatingly difficult to learn the techniques and to keep up with everyone else in any lessons I had (tennis, dance)
*   I spent the entire evenings and weekends catching up on school work

- Simple activities, like going shopping, would exhaust me
- Changing clothing and outfits felt like a huge effort.

The reasons behind these statements I now know relate to all ASD-type problems including executive function.

My limitations with executive function contribute to my lack of motivation. Sometimes it is just a lot easier *not* to do something. The task of just going to the supermarket to buy a few items involves many steps:

getting ready
remembering keys, money, bike lock
taking the correct amount of money
remembering my shopping list
locking up my bike outside the shop
navigating around the shop
working out how to use the self-checkout
packing my items in a sensible way
remembering to put my wallet safely away
remembering where my bike is
unlocking it
putting keys away
and going home.

If I end up having to talk to anybody when I am on my way to or from the supermarket or when I am there, such as a shop assistant or anyone who makes small talk, my social anxiety and social communication impairments will surface too. When this happens unexpectedly, it disrupts my executive function, which can only be at its best when I am following my plan exactly. I have frequently gone to the shop to buy something or to the cash point to take some money out but if somebody starts talking to me it deters me completely, so much so that I can even forget my PIN number!

I am fortunate to have been able to arrange my life in such a way that I usually have enough mental energy to be able to execute executive function should I have to cope with the unexpected. In other periods of my life I never had enough energy.

When I have tasks to undertake, one of my important considerations is **how I can conserve as much energy as possible.** That is why I prefer people who help me stay within my comfort zone, such as allowing me to meet at a time that fits my routine, or in a place I am familiar with, or to do an activity that I am used to in familiar surroundings, in order to minimise the amount of mental energy usage.

Sensory issues also make me less motivated to do things. A lot of environments cause sensory overload. Having to look 'presentable' is another deterrent because washing and dressing are just more steps that use executive function. I like being inside my house and going out on my own without the fuss of bothering with my appearance.

I have learned that **I have to downscale** in order to function best so **I live a very simple minimalist life.** Some of my strategies are that:

- Doing a minimal number of things each day
- Keeping the structure of every day the same or to do the same things every day
- Keeping my responsibilities and commitments to a minimum and prioritising the things that matter most
- Keeping daily transitions to a minimum
- Keeping myself in a quiet, minimalistic environment
- Recognising my comfort zone activities and sticking to these

Different, busy or disruptive days or weeks mean that I am far more likely to get things wrong or forget things because I am exhausted and overwhelmed. There is no more mental energy left for executive function.

I wonder whether a reason why socialising is so difficult for me is because a lot of my executive function is being used up on all the other aspects that surround the socialising, as opposed to just the socialising. These might include being preoccupied with getting somewhere on time and trying to reduce the amount of sensory overload in the journey I take. My brain is working away on these aspects rather than allowing me to relax and just enjoy the socialising. So another tip I have learned is that, if **I want to enjoy socialising, it has to be easy, convenient and in minimalist surroundings.** As mentioned, the best relationships I am able to maintain are with people who do not take me outside my comfort zone.

I would like to give the following advice to autistic people:

Whenever you are going to do an activity it might help for you to think, "How can I make this activity as *easy* as possible?" Some ideas might be:

getting ready the night before
using a payment card instead of handling cash
driving or getting a lift or walking instead of using public transport
only going for a short amount of time
going somewhere that you are familiar with or with someone you know
fitting the activity inside your routine
and taking your own food.

If somebody wants to see me, for example, I try to get them to come to me, as it cuts out the amount of executive function I have to use as I do not have to worry about the travelling arrangements and unfamiliar environments.

Life for me is all about **cutting out all the steps that can be cut out** and I have become very efficient at doing that!

Transitions

A transition is *a shift from one thing to another.* It can refer to: an environment (such as a room, building, moving outside to inside and from inside to outside) or activities (such as entering and coming out of the shower, moving from one task to another, changing clothes, even being quiet to having a conversation).

I have noticed that I get exhausted and suffer from terrible headaches after long or dynamic days. I believe it is to do with not just the amount of socialising, but also how many transitions have taken place that day.

A typical day for me might look like this in terms of the number of transitions (T) and environments (E):

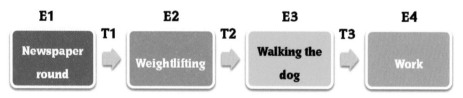

It is a personal view what an individual considers to be 'an environment' and 'a transition'. This is how it is for me. The point I want to make is that there are only a few environments and transitions that I have to deal with on a daily basis now compared to how my life was previously. The school day is a good example when I think about how many different rooms and lessons a child has to contend with:

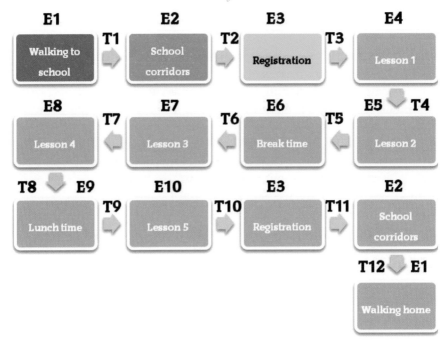

Encountering too many different environments and going through too many transitions makes me feel very overwhelmed. It really is too much for me and I am glad I now recognise this.

My parents would often take my sister and me out at weekends. We used to go to different shops, garden centres and see family friends all across one weekend. I used to hate it and have tantrums. I used to say that it was "boring", but what I really meant, and what I am now understanding, is that it was stressful and exhausting.

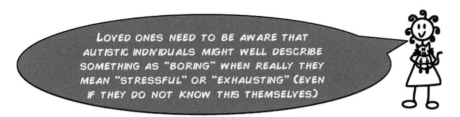

LOVED ONES NEED TO BE AWARE THAT AUTISTIC INDIVIDUALS MIGHT WELL DESCRIBE SOMETHING AS "BORING" WHEN REALLY THEY MEAN "STRESSFUL" OR "EXHAUSTING" (EVEN IF THEY DO NOT KNOW THIS THEMSELVES)

Minimising the number of transitions and environments that I encounter each day is a very good way to help manage my fatigue.

Different environments are tiring for all sorts of reasons, such as:
* Sensory regulation – having to regulate and adjust senses to different environments
* Social expectations – if I have gone from being in a solitary

environment to a social one, what sort of social situation is it and how do I now have to behave? If I have gone from one social environment to another one, how is it different and how do I have to behave now? (We have to behave differently in different social environments and remembering and applying those rules is exhausting)

• Executive function – what do I need to do here? What did I come here for? Am I on time?

I try to keep the number of transitions and environments minimal. I do this by **always walking or cycling** everywhere, as these methods of getting from A to B are far less exhausting for me than taking a bus or a train. If you remember from my first book, I was already noticing that having minimal transitions were helpful because I said that **I preferred to do one thing a day.** I now understand better why this is important. I *can* do multiple things in a day, but I much prefer not to, and if I have to, I schedule them with care.

Managing transitions at home is important too. There are little things I do during the day that will ensure the number of transitions are minimised. For example, I do not like changing my clothes. This means that when I wake up I change from wearing pyjamas straight into my exercise clothes and carry on my day wearing those same exercise clothes, until it is time to do weightlifting. After weightlifting, I usually do not change my clothes again until bed time, when I change into my pyjamas. The transition of changing clothes may also explain why some children are reluctant to get out of their school clothes at the end of the school day. A trick would be to have clothes that are versatile enough for home and work life so that you only have to wear one outfit! I also either shower in the evening right before putting on my pyjamas or shower earlier in the day but change into pyjamas immediately afterwards (so that I do not have to change yet again at night) which means one less transition.

I also prefer to wash my hair at the same time as bathing even though it is a massively uncomfortable task. It takes twice as long, but I do not think I could go through hair and body washing separately.

Sensory processing

I wanted to include sensory processing inside this chapter on executive function because I believe that if a person is physically uncomfortable (because they are not able to regulate their senses) then it means they will not use their executive function as well.

IF YOU ARE ANXIOUS OR OVER STIMULATED THEN YOU ARE NOT USING EXECUTIVE FUNCTION PROPERLY BECAUSE, FOR EXAMPLE, YOU ARE TOO FOCUSED ON GETTING AWAY FROM THE SITUATION

Sensory processing abilities can be summarised as being *how physically uncomfortable a person is at any given time.* I have always been oversensitive to lots of sensations but never realised there was a name for my oversensitivity until I learned about ASD.

Sensory regulation is how quickly one can get comfortable at any given time. Neurotypical people take a fairly short amount of time (usually it is immediate) for their sensory system to adjust to their environment.[9] So, for example, if they go from outside a building to inside and inside is too warm or noisy, they might notice this difference for a moment but their senses will adjust very quickly so that the sound is no longer too noisy or the temperature is no longer too warm. Often, their senses adjust so quickly that they do not even notice.

Sensory processing	How physically uncomfortable a person is at any given time
Sensory regulation	How quickly a person can become comfortable

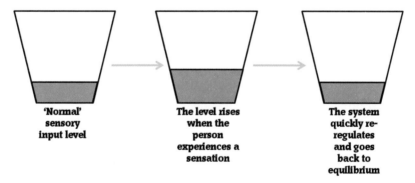

'Normal' sensory input level   **The level rises when the person experiences a sensation**   **The system quickly re-regulates and goes back to equilibrium**

This is what I call the neurotypical sensory bucket. It shows that neurotypical people generally adjust quite quickly to the sensations in their environment.

Neurotypical people also, of course, have better awareness of their own senses and have the skills to know what to do if something is too uncomfortable. It would not be uncommon for an autistic person to not

9 Rowe, A (2016). Asperger's Syndrome: Meltdowns and Shutdowns 2. London: Lonely Mind Books. 53-37.

even think to take off their coat nor to open a window, even if the room they were in was very hot. **A life skill for an autistic person is to learn how to recognise when their body might be uncomfortable** (even if their brain does not realise) and to know what they can do in order to feel better. An environment might be stressful and exhausting, not only because a person cannot regulate their senses well, but also because of the inability to recognise and resolve their sensory discomfort.

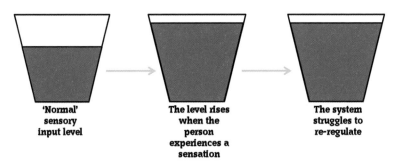

'Normal'
sensory
input level

The level rises
when the
person
experiences a
sensation

The system
struggles to
re-regulate

This is what I call the ASD sensory bucket. It shows that autistic people have difficulty regulating their senses. If the level goes too high, the bucket can even overflow.

Most neurotypical people, as far as I can observe (again, it is just empirical evidence), seem to not have any problems with the sensations they encounter in normal daily life. As an example, when I go into my place of work, I find it very overwhelming because there are a lot of people moving about. This can make my vision go blurry or make me feel dizzy. Sounds, acoustics and echoes inside the room can hurt my ears. There might be so many different sounds that I struggle to differentiate between them all. Smells, such as the fragrance a colleague is wearing or their body wash (and certain foods!), can be massively overpowering.

My observations, however, seem to tell me that my colleagues do not experience our environment in the same way. I have very rarely heard anyone comment that a sensation is overly uncomfortable. Occasionally someone might comment on how loud something is but I notice that *to acknowledge something is uncomfortable is very different from feeling that it actually is.*

I think lots of people might acknowledge that something is uncomfortable but they are not left with physical pain or symptoms of anxiety (fast heartbeat, sweating, trembling, muscle tension) that linger for a long time afterwards.

Perhaps it could just be because most neurotypical people realise that it is not socially appropriate to complain about the intensity of a sensation, but an autistic person might complain anyway!

Nowadays, sensory processing impairments do not affect me as much as they used to. I understand a lot more about why I found school and university so unpleasant because of the sensory input in those environments. I can now control most of the sensory input that I am exposed to. In my house I am alone most of the time. When I do go out, I tend to **go out early in the morning** when it is quiet. I choose to deliver my newspapers as early as I can when the roads are quieter. I am careful about the situations I participate in and politely **decline going anywhere that is crowded, noisy or is going to be very hot and stuffy.**

I find the world very busy, loud and disorientating. People and vehicles are very unpredictable. **I wear earplugs** a lot of the time. In addition to sound, I have an extremely sensitive olfactory system so I notice things such as fragrances which are sadly very popular with other people! On my newspaper round one of the drop offs is inside a block of flats. If I am doing the round late and go into the block I sometimes smell the scent of someone's fragrance lingering in the stairway. It is another reason why I prefer to do the newspaper round as early as possible because I want to avoid – what are to me – nasty scents like that.

I have managed to adapt my life to lessen the impact of having sensory issues. Doing the newspaper round and going for walks first thing in the morning are two adaptations I have made. Being self-employed and being able to **work from home** helps enormously with being more physically comfortable.

I have learned that **having control over sensation** (such as noise, smell, physical experience) is really important. I have come up with the following strategy to help me cope with sensation:

I can cope with sensation much better if I know the answer to those 5 questions. Here is an example:

Stitches example

When I broke my finger, I had to have stitches put in. My mum made the procedure a lot easier for me because, as the nurse was doing, it my mum was giving me the information I needed. My mum sat next to me and gave a running commentary of what was going on such as "the nurse is going to put the first stitch in now" (my eyes were closed, my hood was up, as I was so frightened) and "the last stitch has been done". **I have difficulty knowing when something has ended unless someone explicitly tells me.** My mum was also able to describe how having stitches put in my finger might feel before it happened. This helped me imagine what it was going to feel like.

A simpler example of this strategy would be a fire alarm drill. I will feel far less anxious if I am told:

* What is going to happen (fire drill)
* When it is going to happen (e.g. 9am on Monday)
* What it might feel like (e.g. "loud bells ringing in very quick succession")
* How long it is going to last (e.g. 30 seconds)
* When it has ended (e.g. the teacher, colleague or shop assistant will explicitly state "The fire alarm test is now complete" so that I know for sure that the alarm has stopped.)

Often, it is the *unpredictability* of sensation that makes me so uncomfortable. If some aspects can be made predictable it can really help.

Unknown sensations are terrifying so I always want to have some idea of what something is going to feel like (physically as well as emotionally, which I talked about in a previous chapter). The first time I had my blood pressure taken I was frightened because I did not know how it was going to feel. For a GP to have said, "It will get tighter and tighter until it is at maximum tightness and at this point you'll feel your pulse and then it'll be released and you'll feel normal again" would have been helpful. Before the blood pressure check, it would also have been helpful for a GP to have suggested that I do my own research on the internet to determine what having blood pressure taken might feel like.

There are some sensations that really stress me but, if I do them myself, they do not stress me nearly as much. **Doing things myself** allows me some control over the sensation I need to know about (such as what is going to happen, when something will start and duration). For example, the sound of the vacuum cleaner usually makes my ears hurt unbearably but if I use the vacuum cleaner myself I can tolerate it. A neurotypical person might be able to relate if they think about taking off a plaster themselves versus someone else taking it off for them. If they do it themselves they are in control of the sensation.

If someone else has to do something **it helps a lot if they at least tell me what they are going to do and when.** Then I have a choice over what actions I can take e.g. if somebody is going to do the vacuuming then I can put my earplugs in or I can close the door, or I can go out of the room and choose to do something else. When I was at school or at work people sometimes did the vacuuming at unpredictable times, without any warning, and without any way for me to 'socially appropriately' escape.

Some of the difficulties I have had when going to the hairdresser, the GP, or the osteopath is that they are unlikely to talk through what they are doing in the way that I need. A lot of professionals carry out their procedures without communicating what they are doing and I find that really hard. **I always try to tell people what I need** to know in order to feel less anxious. A good practitioner will oblige. I am a bit more tolerant than I once was and do not expect someone to automatically know what my needs are if I have not informed them. Even if I do not always feel confident enough to tell people in detail, **I still always tell them that I am autistic.**

There are strategies that I use to make sensory discomfort easier for me such as: wearing earplugs, moving to a different space, going out at quiet times of the day and so on. It is helpful to be able to work flexibly to allow me to go out at these quieter times. I would find it (and have found it) much more stressful to have to go out to the bank or go shopping at busy times such as at lunchtime and at weekends. Today, for example, I went to the bank at 11.15am and, as expected, it was empty because everyone else was at work!

As you know, I can't stand the smell of B.A.N.A.N.A.s.[10] In public, I really have no control over whether or not people eat them. The only thing I can really do is move away if somebody decides to eats a B.A.N.A.N.A. However, that is not always seen as an appropriate way to behave if, for example, I am at work or in a classroom. If I am on a train, I will move carriage as soon as someone starts eating one.

---

10 I dislike them so much and I dislike the word too!

Summary of what I have learned about executive function:

- Most actions that I do require very aware thought and conscious effort
- In order to lessen this effort, I live a very minimalistic life involving minimal transitions and minimal environments
- In order to lessen this effort, I have a routine and make plans
- I have sensory processing problems. My sensory system does not work as well as other people's sensory systems, so I try to minimise the sensory input I am exposed to, or I try to keep it within my control and as predictable as I can

WHAT i HAVE LEARNED ABOUT COMMUNICATION

Two-way
Tone of voice and body language
A different way of seeing things

Two-way

Up until very recently I did not understand the significance of communication. I took the same attitude towards communication that I took towards executive function - which was that I did not bother to learn much about it because I thought it did not apply to me and my life. I just thought, even though I am quiet, when I do speak I am always clear in what I say. I say what I mean and mean what I say and do what I say I am going to do. I only speak when I have got something to say. Surely my communication is good enough? Well, yet again I have missed out on so much! Since teaching myself about communication I can confidently agree with what this wise person once said: "Communication is everything. Everything is communication".

The first thing I have learned is that, even if *you* are a good communicator, if the person you are talking to is not, there will still be plenty of misunderstandings. I have learned that communication is two way and that it is the responsibility of both people in any relationship to learn to communicate effectively with each other.

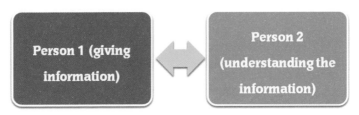

I have also learned that a good communicator is also one who can adapt their own communication to get the best from the other person. I have learned that the manner I communicate with one person might suffice but that I may need to communicate differently with someone else. **Being able to adapt the way that I communicate with a person is a skill** that I am learning. As an example, with some people I am very blunt and to the point, I do not even ask them how they are, yet they respond really well and enjoy talking to me. Other people have considered me slightly insensitive if I communicate with them in that way, so I have to be a bit more chatty. Some people do not like to communicate using text and email, they like to speak in person or on the phone, so I communicate with them via those methods.

There are some general rules for being a good communicator but it is up to an individual to adapt those rules depending on who the other person is. Even if I consider *myself* to be a good communicator, if I cannot communicate to someone in the way they best understand and respond, then I need to improve my communication.

This insight has been especially helpful in my job as my work can involve managing people. For example, in order to get the best from certain people I need to give them lots of feedback and praise, which contrasts with the way that *I* am. *I* work best with other people when they do *not* give me lots of feedback and praise. This is because I do not want much interaction at all – good or bad. I work best with people who leave me to my own devices and keep contact to a minimum.

Tone of voice and body language

Another thing that I have learned about communication is that it is not entirely about words. For example, when I talk to people I tend to be very clear, concise and to the point (this is a trait that many autistic people have). I say exactly and entirely what I mean through words. People have even told me that they like me *because* I am straightforward and say exactly what I mean!

However, words are just one aspect of communication. The other aspects of communication are body language and tone of voice. There is

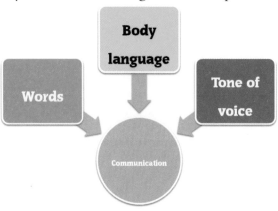

even a theory that body language accounts for a larger proportion of communication than words.

Whereas I know intellectually what positive, correct body language and tone of voice might be, I still have a lot of trouble interpreting and 'reading' other people's body language, as well as my own. This means that other people can have a lot of trouble communicating with me. I am learning **to take more notice of body language and tone of voice** (both in myself and in others) even though my natural style is to communicate solely through very direct words.

A different way of seeing things

Although everybody is an individual, for the purpose of this book, if we assume that most neurotypical people communicate in a similar way because they have a common way of thinking, understanding and responding, then we can understand why someone who is autistic, and who has a different way of thinking and communicating, will really struggle with the most basic interaction and small talk that occurs in daily life.

Post office example

I went to buy something from a local shop. When I arrived the shop was closed and there was a sign on the door that said <Gone to the post office. Back in 5 minutes>

This sort of note always confuses me as they do not state what time the person left so I never know how long that 5 minutes is actually going to be. Intellectually, the longest waiting time it could be would be 4 minutes 59 seconds if they had only just left a second ago. On this occasion I decided to wait.

The post office is about 20 metres to the left of the shop, so I stood outside the shop facing to the left, waiting and expecting the shop assistant to come from that direction. About 15 minutes later he appeared but from the right not the left! It completely confused me!

I said to him, "But the post office is the other way."

He replied, "I went to the one in town."

Then he opened the door and just carried on as usual.

All I could think to myself was, "Well going to that other post office does not take 5 minutes. So why did he write "back in 5 minutes" on the sign?"

It was only later, when I got home and told my parents about this, that a number of other things were brought to my attention, including:

- People sometimes put signs that say 'gone to the post office' even if they do not actually go to the post office. 'Post office' can mean anywhere
- The shop assistant may not have even gone to the post office and it may have been considered impolite for me to question where he had gone
- In some circumstances "5 minutes" just means a short amount of time, not literally 5 minutes.

This is one example of why communication and navigating the world is so confusing. None of these points had even occurred to me at the time. It is only later, often only when I talk to other people, that I can see different perspectives.

My way of viewing the world seems to be very different from other people's and I struggle to even imagine how someone else experiences things. It is actually near impossible until they point out to me how they view the world. So often, if I do not talk to people about confusing situations like this, I will never understand. I am therefore learning **to talk to my family about the things that confuse me** because it helps me develop theory of mind, stops me ruminating, and it gives them a chance to teach me how I can make slight alterations to my own behaviour. For example, I now realise that questioning someone about where they have been and how long it took them, in a similar way to the post office example, might be taken as a sign of being 'nosey' and impolite. I would never have known that someone might think this of me, because I was just saying something that made logical sense.

I have lots of misunderstandings with my dad when I say things that are very logical because he cannot see where I am coming from and he is interpreting something else instead. He gets very cross with me and I find it upsetting and frustrating. I ask "why?" and "what do you mean?" a lot and he can take it as me being difficult or deliberately annoying, whereas I am asking because I genuinely do not understand what he said and feel confused. Maybe he feels exasperated and realises that he has poor communication skills!

Another example might be when I go into the shop to buy a takeaway mug of hot chocolate. This is what has happened to me on a number of occasions:

Hot chocolate example

I say to the shop assistant, "Please could I have a mug of hot chocolate?"

The shop assistant replies, "No hot chocolate today, sorry!"

When this happens I just freeze, unless I have anticipated this sort of situation and have an alternative in my head (such as to order something else or to say "OK, thanks. Bye") I feel like my brain has stopped. So you can see why it is important for me to **think in advance about a situation that I might encounter** so that I can be prepared and know how to react.

The shop assistant then says, "Just kidding! That is £1.80 please."

He proceeds to make the hot chocolate in the machine.

This situation, and others like it, happen to me many times. Each time I am left utterly confused and out of my depth in terms of social understanding. I do not know how to 'read' these situations and how to respond to them in the moment. I cannot see the joke!

Neurotypical people are able to pick up on the shop assistant's body language, or his smile, in order to work out that he is not being serious and he is joking. They would know what to say or what to do in response. In fact, sometimes nothing has to be said at all, except for a laugh or a roll of your eyes! But, if you are like me, you cannot work out if he is joking or being serious. If he is joking, why would he be joking about something like this? I am confused and terrified. I am now prepared for this kind of situation because it has happened so many times, however I still find it extremely awkward and have no natural way to respond.

I use up a lot of mental energy in these situations trying to work out what is going on. They require a lot of communication skills for someone with a communication disorder like me.

Another example of one of the communication difficulties I have would be when I ask someone a question. I feel that I ask very clear, specific and literal questions. But when I do this, other people tend not to answer them. I will get an answer to something that I did not ask. I suspect what is actually going on is that they have heard what I said and have unintentionally altered and responded to what they *think* I have said, or what they *think* that I meant, but not what I *actually* said or meant. For example, if I ask my dad when he gets home from work if he has managed to get any corn flakes, he might say "I've just got home!" I am just asking a specific, clear, literal question. I am not sure why he is talking about just getting home. How is that relevant? All he has to say is "yes" or "no". Unless he explains to me what he means, I do not understand.

What people say in response is not always what I expect.

Some neurotypical people have a tendency to read between the lines, when I really just want a straight answer to what I have asked. A neurotypical directing a question to another neurotypical, who has the same thought process, would automatically read between the lines and the one asking the question would be anticipating and expecting that the one answering the question would take it in the way they implied, and will answer it in the way they are expecting. This sounds very confusing but it does make sense! I will try to give an example:

Neurotypical Person 1: ("I know if I ask this then they'll mention C, which is what I want")
Neurotypical Person 1: "Is A related to B?"
Neurotypical Person 2: ("Oh, they want me to talk about C")
Neurotypical Person 2: "C is…"

Compare that to:

ASD Person: ("I want to know about A and B")
ASD Person: "Is A related to B?"
Neurotypical Person: ("Oh, they want me to talk about C")
Neurotypical Person: "C is…"
ASD Person: ("Why are they talking about C? That is not what I asked. I'm confused")

So sometimes **I have to change the way I communicate and change the way I ask something** so that I can get the response I want. But this requires a lot of social skills and social energy and is incredibly difficult:

ASD Person: ("If I ask this, I anticipate that they will mention C, which is
not what I want. I want them to talk about A and B. So I will ask about C
instead")
ASD Person: "What do you think about C?"
Neurotypical Person: "Well, A and B are…"

I am learning that I have had to, and still have to, do a lot of work to
develop my own communication skills in order to communicate with
anyone. I am learning that the key to good communication – *especially
if the other person is a poor communicator and will not change* – is sometimes
adapting one's communication and thinking style so that it is similar to
the other person's (just as I did in the above example) So, sometimes, good
communication is less about being very clear and literal and more about
matching someone else's style of communication.

But, I still think **being very clear, concise and literal is the best way to
be,** as in the end, this minimises chances of miscommunication, at least on
my end.

Being unable to read between the lines makes communication hard
for me. For example, my dad saying to me "the house is a mess", to
me is a *statement.* He is merely observing. But it is only later, when he
comes home from work very cross, moaning that I had not done any
vacuuming, that I realise that what he actually meant that morning was,
"Please could you do the vacuuming today whilst I am at work?"

I wish people would be literal as well. A lot of people make assumptions
over what I am asking. I wish they would answer me literally.

"What time is it?" I ask.
"Why, do you have to be somewhere?" someone replies. Or "Stop being
so desperate to go!"

I am merely asking for the time.

The problem with literal thinking is that many people are not literal
thinkers, so communicating with people who are not, causes
misunderstandings. Intellectually, I might know, or have an inkling, that
what a person is saying is not to be taken literally, but it still conjures up
the literal image or depiction in my mind and it is hard to focus on
anything else. It is confusing and distracting because I cannot follow the

conversation. I am still thinking about what was said previously and ruminating over whether or not it made sense and why they chose to use that particular phrase or word and whether that was what they really meant or did they mean something else instead? No wonder conversations are exhausting (in the same way that last, long sentence perhaps felt exhausting to read!).

Sometimes I take what someone says literally and then get totally lost. One of my managers is a vet and he once showed me a bag of cat food and said to me, "My cat's on this". I looked at the bag and actually genuinely thought the picture of the cat on the bag was his cat. I said, "Is that your cat?" Then he clarified that what he actually meant was that his cat eats that particular type of food!

Even when someone says something that I know they don't mean literally, it still puts that picture in my mind.

The more interactions I have in a day, the more chances there are for confusing conversations, the more my brain has to work. No wonder I feel very tired after socialising!

Taking people's words literally also makes me a bit naïve and vulnerable. Because I am this way, I do tend to trust people but, since coming to understand my condition and my impairment, it has made me more aware that I am likely to be naïve and I think I am a bit more cautious around people now and a bit less trusting. It is another benefit from understanding yourself more. You can be more cautious about the intentions of others.

The way I naturally process and understand language does not quite match up to the way other people express language. I think one of the biggest reasons why I appear quiet, blank or unempathetic at times is just because I do not understand what a person is saying:

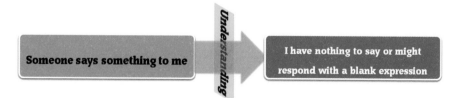

Another example of missing the meaning of things and focusing only on what has been said might be if I had planned to do something, and I receive an email that says 'Sincere apologies, I am not well today', which to me just means that the person is not well. The unspoken implication is that the planned activity has been cancelled. In the past, I would have probably still turned up to the activity.

My dad asked me to help him move some furniture. His actual question was, "Can you help me move this some time?" to which I replied "Yes". A few days later he was moaning at me because the furniture had not been moved. In my mind, he had not specified a day or a time. I have no idea what "some time" means. If he just said *when* he wanted it moved I could agree and we could have done it. **I have learned to be a bit more intuitive** and reply to him, "*When* would you like to move it?" However, due to my difficulties with social imagination, it is very hard to do this. In my mind, I had replied to him literally by saying that yes, I could help him move it at some time.

Vagueness is also a major problem. Most people are too vague and because we do not share the same thinking style I cannot keep up with them. For example, if my dad comes in the house just as I am about to go out and says "It's not very nice out there", I am not sure what he means. "Nice" could mean a lot of things. It is a very vague description that is not even exclusively linked to the weather. "Nice" is also subjective so was he talking about "not very nice" for him or for me? I have learned that what he is usually referring to is the weather. When he says "not very nice" he means that it is raining outside. I only know this because I am familiar with him and the way he uses words. But you can imagine how difficult and confusing a conversation can be for me with people I do not know! In answer to what my dad said, I say: "Do you mean it's raining?" and he will say "Yes". Nevertheless, **I still wish people would say exactly what they mean and use the right words.** It would lead to more effective communication (less words, less possibility of miscommunication, less thinking for both people) if for example my dad had said the first time, "It's raining outside".

Last night I had a migraine and went to bed feeling awful. When I woke up this morning and went downstairs, my dad said to me: "How are you feeling today?"

I said: "A bit better, thank you."
He said: "What do you want to do today?"

This comment confused me. I was not sure what he was asking me. Again, it was too vague. What do I want to do today can cover a number of things ranging from do I want to work on my book, do my accounts, walk the dog, do weightlifting, see my mum or my gran or anything else?

I took the initiative to ask him to clarify. I said:
"What do you mean?"

He said: "Do you still want to walk the dog?" (We had last night planned to walk the dog together in the morning.)

In this example my dad had initially asked me two questions: 1) how I was feeling, and 2) what I wanted to do. I had problems linking the two and did not realise that how I was feeling had anything to do with what I wanted to do. I took them as separate questions.

It would have been helpful for my dad to reword the above to:

"You were not well last night. Are you feeling well enough today to walk the dog together as we had planned?"

To me that is much clearer!

I wish that people would be straightforward in what they are asking and what they want to know. It is very hard for me to work out what people mean and causes far more confusion than there need be. If only people communicated better!

I think another common problem for autistic people is the ability to link sentences and see the bigger picture, or story of what someone is saying. Autistic people often focus on each sentence or topic as a single item. Perhaps another reason why I appear to lack emotion when I talk to people is that I do not fully understand how what they are saying relates to the whole because I am processing one line at a time.

There is a lot to be said for getting comfortable with someone though! I find I am less likely to feel confused with people I am familiar with because, even if they are confusing, I can anticipate that they are going to be confusing. Sometimes I am able to hear what someone I know is saying, and understand that they do not mean what they are saying and mean something else instead. But even if I am confused, at least with people I know I feel more comfortable about asking them to repeat or clarify. With others, I get stuck wondering if what they said is what they meant, or did they mean something else? Then I have to deal with anxiety about having to ask them to clarify what they meant. If I ask most people to clarify their remarks, I can get any of these responses:

they think I am a bit slow
they think I am someone who does not pay attention
they laugh at me for asking them to keep repeating
they think I am partially deaf.

I need people to be very specific and very literal in what they say when they talk to me. If someone wants me to do something, then I need them to ask not hint, otherwise I will not do it. If someone wants me to make a comment, give feedback or give a response, they need to be very clear and explicit and say that they expect a response. Generally people will not hear from me unless it is clear they want a response. So for example, if my manager sends me an email asking me to do something, I will just get on and do it. I will not necessarily tell him that I have done it *unless* he has said "please let me know when it is done".

I believe that both neurotypicals and autistic people can be bad at communicating. A lot of neurotypical people are only used to communicating with others like themselves. They have little or no experience of having to adapt the way they communicate when speaking to someone who is different.

Something that I have come to truly appreciate is that, if somebody does not have a communication disability or they do not have autism, then to imagine what it must be like to have these problems must be extremely difficult. I always say, for a person to feel empathy, they have to be able to *imagine* what it must be like for others. It must be really hard for people without any communication problems to be able to imagine what it is like to have a communication problem.

Something that I am also learning is that many of the difficulties I have are more to do with differences in communication, rather than solely being difficulties.

Summary of what I have learned about communication:

- A large number of people are poor at communicating
- A large number of people *think* they are good at communicating but are not
- Just because you are neurotypical it does not mean you are good at communicating
- Just because you have autism it does not mean you are poor at communicating
- Adapting our own communication to match how someone else would like to be communicated to can be helpful
- Differences (rather than difficulties) in communication can cause misunderstandings
- We can all develop our communication skills on an ongoing basis
- Being clear, concise and literal is always a good way for everyone to aim to communicate as, ultimately, this is the way that will reduce the chance of misunderstandings

12/12

WHAT i HAVE LEARNED ABOUT ME

Relationships
Education and working
Weightlifting
General activities
My personality
Accepting me
Self-development
Contentment

I often wonder about my personality and my behaviour and interests and how much influence having ASD has had on me and my life. I used to think that personality and ASD were very separate but now I think that they overlap massively.

I know my ASD affects:

1) *what* I think (e.g. "there is an incorrect apostrophe written on the whiteboard"):

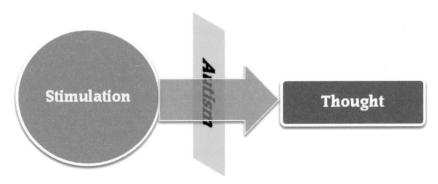

Autism influences what stimulates me.

2) how I think about that thought (e.g. "Why is there an incorrect

apostrophe written on the whiteboard?" "Why is nobody else saying anything?" and then that sole focus on the apostrophe for the remainder of the lesson):

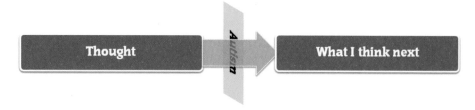

Autism causes my logical, literal, detailed, black and white, repetitive thinking.

3) my responses and reactions to thoughts, feelings and external situations (e.g. "I am not able to say anything about the apostrophe because I do not know how and when to say it and I feel too anxious, etc." so instead I remain silent):

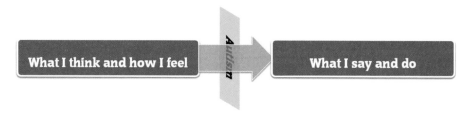

Autism creates a barrier of anxiety and social communication impairments which affects how I respond to my thoughts.

Relationships

I think that even without ASD, I would still be introverted, but I think that I would cope a lot better with social situations. My quietness now probably comes mostly from anxiety and from having such severe difficulty with verbal language, body language and tone of voice. It also comes a bit from not being able to relate to what other people like to talk about. So if I did not have ASD, I would not be anywhere near as anxious, I definitely would not have the communication impairments, and I think I would be able to relate to other people more, so I do not think I would be *as* quiet. One of the hardest things about having ASD is, actually, intellectually seeing how my social life could ("should"?) have been.

ASD means that I am just always on the outside. Activities and socialising always feel too "upsetting" or "difficult". ASD means that I am just too anxious, too shy, too quiet, too solitary, and too different to connect with others as easily as they connect with one another. Even if I was not anxious, shy or quiet, having uncommon thoughts and different interests to others automatically places me on the outside anyway.

Without ASD, I would be a lot less withdrawn and less shut away in my own world and more engaged with the outside world. Crowds, noise, smells, temperature, spontaneity and changes would not affect me as much as they do. I would probably go out a bit more and see friends and do activities that I like but that I tend to currently avoid, (such as going to the theatre) because ASD makes these activities so hard. If I did not have ASD, I probably would not even need to wear earplugs when I was at the theatre. Today my place of work is organising and running the local community fair; I think that I would be there too if I did not have ASD. All other team members are there.

I have felt, and have expressed, so many times throughout my life that I am lonely. Yet I've had so many opportunities to have and make friends and spend time with people. Even recently someone said to me, "There must be so many people who'd love to be your friend".

I am not especially lonely now but I have been. My ASD causes me to feel stressed and to shy away from people who try to befriend me, ask me out, or persist in trying to socialise with me. It is rarely the person that is the problem, it is all the communication, the activity they are proposing, the environment, the time of the day, how it fits into my routine, the organisation required for me to actually leave my house and go and meet them and what to talk about. I know that if I did not have ASD I would not have to think about all these factors all the time when "hanging out" with someone (If I did not have ASD, I would know exactly what "hanging out" means and I would be able to do it!). I always say, I actually really *like* a lot of people very much, yet socialising and having friendships is just really, really intense and challenging.

I have got a few friends now but even maintaining contact with them and arranging to meet up causes me so much difficulty and anxiety. It is just not something that comes naturally at all. I know that if I did not have ASD, I would have a larger social network and I would have a far easier time maintaining my relationships. I may not see or talk to people much, but it would be far more than I do now. ASD is what causes me to struggle in getting comfortable with the level any potential friends want us both to be on or the level they expect me to be on with them. The diagram below demonstrates what I am trying to say. Let us say that if I did not have ASD, levels 1, 2 and 3 (especially level 3) would be far easier for me to reach and more frequently reached too:

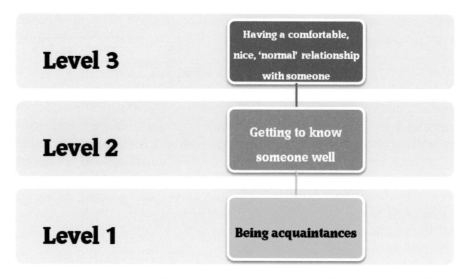

Level 3	Having a comfortable, nice, 'normal' relationship with someone
Level 2	Getting to know someone well
Level 1	Being acquaintances

The people I know would describe me as "someone they never actually get to see". I do not like this description. I know that if I did not have ASD, people would not describe me in that way.

Education and working

If I did not have ASD, I would not have as much difficulty working and studying. I think I would have still done my chemistry degree and would have achieved the same results, but perhaps by working less hard!

I honestly do not think I would be entrepreneurial because I think ASD has made me an entrepreneur. All the skills associated with being entrepreneurial are linked to my ASD traits. Maybe if I did not have ASD, I would just have a 'normal' working life (and I would be content with that). A normal job would not exhaust me as much, so I would be able to maintain a typical job in addition to having emotionally-fulfilling hobbies and relationships. It is important to me that my work is emotionally fulfilling, but even if it is not, so long as I have the energy to obtain emotional fulfilment outside of work, it would bother me less. I think that if I did not have ASD, I would have this energy. Maybe I would have progressed a career in science.

Weightlifting

If I did not have ASD, I think I would still like Olympic weightlifting but I do not think I would be as good at weightlifting as I am now because I believe that my performance as a weightlifter is linked to my ASD traits.

Perhaps if I did not have ASD I would also be able to cope with going to a public gym.

Perhaps if I did not have ASD I would have a broader exercise and keeping fit regime rather than keeping to the very specific, limited, repetitive movements of weightlifting.

General activities

I will briefly talk about 'general activities' and by this I mean the things that all people have to do, such as going to the GP, shopping and appointments… etc. All of these activities cause me a large amount of anxiety and discomfort. If I did not have ASD, I know that these activities would not bother me as much.

Going to the GP, or attending any appointment, causes a lot of problems. These services are highly inaccessible for me. For example, I have a lot of difficulty using the telephone. It makes me anxious and I have trouble understanding what people are saying. It is the standard way to communicate for most neurotypical people. For example, I email my osteopath to book my appointments but sometimes they don't reply, and if I bring this up in person, my osteopath replies, "It's better if you phone instead. It's the easiest way". This solution which is so simple and obvious to him (and other neurotypical people) is not an ideal solution for me.

It is my ASD that makes me so fixated on plans and times. So for most people, when they visit the GP and the GP is 10 minutes late, it does not especially bother them, but it really, really affects me. I have learned strategies to cope with this, but if I did not have ASD I know I would not even have had to come up with strategies as it would never be such a major issue!

Changes in plans and spontaneity really bother me. If I did not have ASD, they would still bother me, but nowhere near to the same degree. It is the ASD that causes me to have such rigid thinking and such difficulty in being flexible. It is the ASD that causes me to plan out my day to the hour and to follow my plans through. If I didn't have ASD, I would still be organised and efficient, but if something went 'wrong' there would not be such stressful consequences. I would not be left with that lingering feeling of anxiety for the rest of the day. The entire day would not get ruined.

My personality

I think that I have always had a very strong personality and sense of who I am but my whole life felt as though it was dictated by others. I have been doing things that I was 'supposed' to do rather than what I actually wanted to do. Unfortunately, due to this, my true personality got lost or hidden away. I feel as though I have lived my entire life trying to be somebody that I am not. It was all because I did not understand myself and my ASD as well as being around lots of people who were not empathetic.

For example, teachers and other students considered it "strange" or "wrong" that I was heavily into rap music when I was younger. However, if they had taken a more positive interest in me, they would have realised I was gifted at writing rap lyrics. I could have taught them a lot of fascinating things about cadences and the meaning of words in songs (not the rude words that a lot of rap music is associated with!). Instead, their reactions meant I never told anyone about what I did and pretended to like normal pop music like everybody else. No one ever judged me if I said I liked pop music. They thought that was a good thing to like. Happily, I am back listening to rap music and writing rap lyrics now!

My strong personality has returned and I like myself. I think that my true personality only really shows once strategies are found and reasonable adjustments are made in daily life so that I feel less anxious and am better able to communicate. This helps me come out of my glass jar. Or maybe ASD is a sort of shell that inhibits personality. Other people who can communicate with me in the way that I need will get to see my true personality. I wonder if this all highlights the importance of having a diagnosis (or at least *recognising* that you

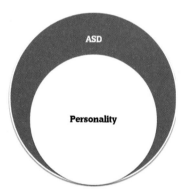

ASD is the shell that inhibits personality.

might have ASD), because for me, without knowing about ASD, I would not have been able to come up with the strategies that I have written about in this book.

Something I have been thinking about is how similar my autism and my personality are. Maybe I am one of the more fortunate autistic people because my autism actually fits quite well with my personality. Autism gives me lots of challenges, but it does not restrict me too much, because I am genuinely not interested in lots of the things that I would find really difficult anyway. Perhaps if I was more extroverted or had different desires and goals in my life I would feel more frustrated and held back by autism. For example, if I wanted to be a vet or a doctor, or if I had dreams of travelling around the world, or if I wanted to have children, or have a big social life I am sure my autism would frustrate me. I would struggle to keep up with the demands that come with these activities (being very busy, socialising, problem solving, being able to adapt to changes, adapting to new environments, having less structure and less Alone Time). Since my desires and goals in life are just to have a quiet, peaceful time at home, doing Olympic weightlifting, caring for my animals and working on my own solitary projects, my autism does not impair me to the extent that I find restrictive. I do not go out and socialise much by *choice* as well as by need. I have not had to excessively change my introversion to fit in with my autism.

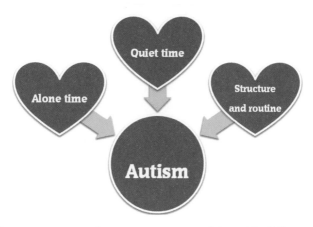

My natural way is to *enjoy* being quiet, peaceful, stable following routine, sameness and structure – those things fit in well and are natural 'friends' of autism anyway.

	Want	Need
Alone Time	✓	✓
Quiet time	✓	✓
Structure and routine	✓	✓

Maybe you would find it helpful to create your own table.

I believe that I am very much the same person that I was when I wrote my first book, but my thoughts and understanding are far more sophisticated and mature now. I also think I have a better understanding and tolerance for other people and all that goes on in the world as opposed to feeling so irritated and disappointed by all things all of the time. I have spent my whole life observing and learning to understand neurotypical behaviour. Ever since I learned that I am not neurotypical, my expectations of the world have been different because I know and accept that there are lots and lots of people who are *not* like me. I think that I used to get very frustrated when people were different, or I would feel very upset when I felt I was not like them, and then I would try to force myself to adapt to them or wish that they would adapt to me. I now understand that some things just cannot be adapted. I accept that I am different. I accept that everyone is different. **I now make a more conscious effort to be considerate and open minded** to other people, rather than being angry, disappointed and judgemental.

Accepting me

I have learned a lot of strategies that help me cope with life. This means that my ASD does not impair me as much as it used to. It is still there, but the point is that if I did not have ASD, I would not have had to create all these strategies in the first place because: 1) I would not have the same problems to such a disabling degree, and 2) I would have flexible thinking skills.

Although I feel I have eventually found a place in the world, it has been incredibly hard to get to this point and I still have plenty of times when I wish I could just have a normal life and do normal activities, not because I want to do them, but because I wish I *did* want to do them. This would help me to integrate better with everything and everyone around me. I have gone through a large proportion of my life having suicidal thoughts, largely because I feel so socially isolated and struggle so much to relate to or fit in with anyone anywhere.

I have tried to participate in normal neurotypical activities, but usually participation leaves me so stressed and exhausted that to maintain that sort of life is unmanageable and intolerable.

My intrinsic thinking and natural desires have always seemed to be at odds with other people. Their needs were to socialise or to at least be far more sociable than I was. Even though I knew this, I still had the thoughts, "Why am I like this?" "Why do I always want to be on my own?" "Why am I so different from other people?" "Why do I not enjoy being with others like other people?" It was excruciating. It is still excruciating, but at least I now have the answer to most of the 'why' questions. It is not easy to have ASD. It has hindered my relationships with others and it has made life far more difficult than it would have been if I had been neurotypical. I am at peace now with how I am because I understand *why*.

I do not have to mask as much anymore. Interestingly, I would suspect that a lot of the masking I was doing during childhood and as a teenager was a coping mechanism as a result of being so overwhelmed. I am not sure if that makes sense. I think I was so exhausted that I completely lost myself, and all I could do was put on a mask and be someone else so that I could navigate through life. At least if I was wearing a mask and doing what everyone else was doing, I had a script and directions to follow. To be myself (so different from everyone else) is a very lonely and confusing experience and I needed to have enough energy and maturity to learn to find my own way. It was only when life got less busy, less social - and I got a bit older - that I had a moment to truly discover who I was and what I needed. So now I know myself a lot more and I have had time and energy to work out my own way in the world. You just do not have this time as a child and young adult as life is so hectic and full of the pressures from education and all the normal struggles that come from puberty and growing up.

For me, **less is better.** Being minimal means fewer relationships, less stimulation, less transitions, minimal attachment to material items together with fewer hobbies and extracurricular activities. I believe, if I can keep things to a minimum, then I have a higher amount of energy every day to enable me to minimise masking and to do the tasks to the best of my abilities and lessen the likelihood of having shutdowns. I think something that is quite hard for other people to understand is that I am content and feel settled with how things are, rather than striving to achieve more or different things. Achievement, whilst important, does not override my wish to remain calm and avoid being under pressure, overwhelmed and anxious.

Since **understanding my needs more and creating a life that fulfils those needs,** I have noticed that if something does happen that causes me stress or overwhelms me, I can recover far more quickly than in the past. Having my needs met has made me very resilient. I remember I used to get physically unwell after doing something that was overwhelming. I even remember I used to have to cancel my newspaper round for the next day if I was doing something really eventful the day before, in anticipation of being so tired that I would not be able to get out of bed. This does not happen anymore. I never have to cancel my newspaper round. It is because I manage all these triggers much more effectively now, and I am much less debilitated by my triggers, because I have more control over my life generally. Because I know myself better, I can pace myself and I am comfortable enough with myself, and with others, to politely decline things that I no longer wish to do or in the past felt I had to do. It means I get enough Alone Time, recharge time and time for weightlifting and other projects, which has come about because I am more able to stick to my routine more closely.

I have also noticed that as I have got older other people accept me more. This has helped me enormously and also helps me to accept myself (and them!). I do not mask as much anymore *because* a lot of people have changed their attitudes. Instead of saying, "You need to get out more", "You should try [this] and [this]" and "Why don't you do [this]? It would be good for you!", *they now say,* "You're an adult now, if you don't want to do something you don't have to; you just have to say no" and "Stop trying to please everyone all the time". Funny how people change once you grow up. It is horrible how much pressure and judgment people put on children and young adults. They do not realise the damage those comments can cause.

People who follow my work understand me more and have more empathy now as well!

Self-development

I think that I have changed very little in comparison to other people of my age. My personality and my lifestyle are very similar to how they have always been. Even if something in my life has changed, I am probably wishing it had not! I have not become more sociable and I have not found new hobbies. My routine is predictable and regular. Perhaps it is because of my autism that I have such a strong sense of identity: I know what I like and dislike, I know my strengths and my challenges, I do not feel I need to try new things, and I am most content when I am doing the same, normal things each day.

I am the same person, I just understand myself and my situation a lot better now, and I finally have connections in the world (true friendships, and a community of people who understand me) unlike how it used to be.

I have also noticed that the strategies often used for 'self improvement' by most people do not seem to work for me, so perhaps neurotypical people develop more quickly or easily, whilst I struggle a lot more, take more time, or do not develop typically 'desirable' traits in typical ways. For example, there have been plenty of times where I 'forced' myself into social situations thinking that my quiet, anxious, introverted self might actually be a closeted extroverted individual that would go into a situation friendless and come out with lots of friends.

When I was little I wanted to go to Drama School because I was convinced that if I attended I would become outgoing and make friends *in the same way that seemed to happen to most other people.* This did not happen to me. In the first lesson I was so anxious and shy that I could not say anything at all and just sat on my own the whole time, ignored and rejected by the others (including the teacher). Afterwards, I had a tantrum with my parents and refused to go to the next lesson. My parents were furious with me because they had paid for the whole term and could not recover the money.

I have forced myself to participate in social activities that other people enjoy, such as parties, cinema, shopping, restaurants, bowling, go-carting... wondering whether, and hoping that, if I did these activities enough, or if I tried harder, I would also be able to enjoy them. Those situations never gave me the outcomes I wished for. All the times I have tried and participated I realise that it is not me and that those things do not 'fit' me.

I have also observed, that neurotypical people, who might on the surface appear *not* to be interested in these things (maybe because they appear to be 'outsiders' instead), may also try these sorts of activities and they are far more likely to enjoy them. This is what I mean by neurotypical people who are outsiders being more capable than me of being able to change. I think that neurotypical people are a bit more adaptable than I am and find it easier to come out of their comfort zones. Or maybe their comfort zones are just a lot bigger in the first place.

Neurotypical people may have bigger comfort zones in the first place, or they can see and utilise the benefit of coming out of them.

I feel that my comfort zone is very small and that it is better for me to try to *expand* my comfort zone rather than come out of it:

I prefer to try to expand my comfort zone.

I believe that it is possible to coax a shy neurotypical person out of their shell, but it is far harder to pull an autistic person like me out of their glass jar[11]. Maybe this is because I, and other autistic people, have to use very different strategies in order to come out of our glass jars and change.

I do not seem to change as much as other people and *having to cope with other people changing, whilst I remain the same, is difficult.* If I do want to improve an aspect of myself it has to be done in a different way, otherwise it will not work. For example, I already know for certain that participating in more social activities more frequently does not make me a more sociable person with better social skills.

An autistic person in their glass jar is different to a shy neurotypical person inside their shell.

Perhaps the real key is **learning to differentiate between the situations and activities that will most likely help me develop and improve versus those that are essentially just not a 'fit' for me.** The latter leads to awful feelings of isolation and low self-esteem.

11   Rowe, A (2018). Asperger's Syndrome: Socialising & Social Energy. 2nd ed. London: Lonely Mind Books. 16–20.

Contentment

One positive outcome of understanding myself better is that I now feel more content. My life is based on comfort rather than excitement. I think that many people are not content, or if they are, their content feeling does not last long.

I often wonder why people seem so keen to do things like going out, going on holiday, seeing the latest film and be wearing the latest fashions. I have spoken to a few people about why this might be. My weightlifting friend has a tendency to want to try all sorts of different exercises and I wanted to ask her why. She gave a few reasons but the one I most clearly remember is: "I think society leads us to believe that more, new and different is always better". She is right, it does, and even I have had this mindset. The point is we often find that doing those things does not make us happy. We might think they make us happy, think they *should* make us happy, or hope that they will... but they often do not.

I feel very fortunate that I live a very contented life in comparison with other people. Most of the time, inside my own world, following my own routine and getting on with my own things that interest me. That is when I feel contented. It also explains why I usually want to say "no" when someone suggests we do something together. I do not really feel the need to do anything else because of my contentment.

There are some positives to having ASD even though a lot of it is not positive. I have strong interests and I like routine. When these are combined with my introversion, I have a predictable, simple and quiet life in which I am fulfilled.

I understand now that, when I was younger, one of the reasons I had so much stress and misery was because I was always looking for something else and trying to do something different or be someone I was not, or I was 'forced' to be someone I was not and to do things that were unsuited for me (such as going to school. To this day I still feel I should have been home educated). I need to remain true to myself and build a life based upon my strengths, rather than build a life based upon what I feel *should* be my strengths.

Summary of what I have learned about me:

- Autism forms a large part of my personality
- If I did not have autism, I think that I would have the same personality traits but those traits would be more expressive and therefore people would find it easier to get to know me and me them
- If I did not have autism, I would still be an introvert, but I think I would have a bigger and happier social life
- If I did not have autism, I think I would have the same likes/dislikes, but I would pursue my interests in a different way (and I would not dislike my dislikes so strongly!)
- If I did not have autism, I would be a lot less anxious and I would not have as many communication difficulties
- If I did not have autism I am not sure I would be an entrepreneur
- I have managed to accept who I am because I have managed to create a life which fulfils and maintains my needs, which enables me to function well

EPILOGUE

Well, I have finally finished the book! After it is published, I will not look at it again! I can never look back at any of my old books. I have not once looked back at 'Asperger's and Me' since it was published. I sometimes have people approach me at a conference or send me an email where they reference something that I said in 'Asperger's and Me'. I can never remember! It is too awkward for me to look back at my old work as, although it was all correct at the time, I have learned a lot more since then and now understand a lot more so my views now are a bit different. A book is only true for a moment in time. I have no doubt that there are some things in my previous book that I would now disagree with. Indeed, the same will be said in a few years about this book.

There are some contradictions in this book. I can already identify many parts that contradict each other, but as separate paragraphs they make sense. In addition, writing a book is a bit of an awkward job because it is a *process* not a result. It is written over a period of time during which thoughts and feelings change! So in this book you will get some diversity just because of the time span it took to write. It took three months by the way, for the first draft, in case you are wondering.

Everything you read however is *very honest and very real.*

This book is a collection of all the things I have learned about myself since starting The Curly Hair Project. I had a lot of knowledge already but may not have fully understood the larger picture or significance of what I already knew. I think I have learned a lot, but in a backwards way! For example, I always knew that I was "shy" and "quiet" but what I did not know was the actual reason I am like this is because I am *autistic,* not just because I am introverted. There is a complete difference between being "shy" and having quite a severe social communication impairment stemming from autism.

There is a difference between: 1) knowing that I am a hard worker and that I spend a lot of time working, and 2) understanding that the *reason* I work so hard might be because I have a serious problem with executive function, which means tasks take longer than they ought to, or... that I get preoccupied by the detail in things and lose sight of the bigger picture.

There is a difference between: 1) recognising that sounds hurt my ears and that touches can be unbearable, and 2) understanding that the reason such 'normal' sensations can be so awful for me is that I have a sensory processing disorder.

There is a difference between: 1) knowing that I want to spend a lot of time alone, and 2) understanding that I actually *need* this time alone in order to cope with life's challenges.

So, I hope that this book contains insight and strategies that could help anyone (regardless of whether they are autistic or not). I hope that this book can teach a lot of people some helpful things about life generally.

If you are neurotypical, I am hoping that after reading this book your mind has been opened up to a different way of thinking and perceiving the world. I am hoping that you have become more aware and understanding of the difficulties and anxieties that are atypical. Just because they are unusual they should not be considered less important factors in life.

If you are autistic, I would feel very pleased if you have been able to relate to a lot of what I have said. I always worry that when I write something that people will not be able to relate to me. I panic and then wonder if I really am just completely *insane,* rather than merely autistic?! I hope you have been able to understand yourself better and feel a bit less alone in the world. I hope that some of the strategies I use to have a more enjoyable and fulfilling life, can help you too.

As the years pass, I realise that I am, or have become, an epitome of someone who is autistic. In this book you will read that I am different and that I have quite severe difficulties, yet in daily life no one would think so. The glass jar is always there and I very rarely feel truly connected with people, but at least I now understand this and I can manage these difficulties. I think my problem connecting with people is the most obvious symptom of autism. Even positive interaction does not always lead to the feeling of being connected. Nearly every time I am outside my home, I feel myself retreating into my glass jar. I do not want to talk to anyone. I wish I could get away from the situation. I have felt like withdrawing more or less through my entire life.

I can appear 'OK' on the outside but I struggle in the majority of situations. When I am away from home I am always wishing to count down the time until I can get home. I am often working out what the earliest "polite" time is that I can leave. It does not matter where or what it is, from being at a film festival, radio studio, attending a university lecture, going to the theatre or seeing a friend. I always look forward to it being over.

Occasionally, I will enjoy connecting with people and doing activities, but I still always feel an outsider, or as though there is an invisible barrier like having the glass jar around me that other people do not have. It is how I know I have ASD.

Although I like to think of myself as a friendly and a nice person, the reality is that I am very isolated and keep myself at a distance from others and from the world. I will be direct and pleasant enough with people if they contact me, but generally people will not hear much from me at all.

Because I spend a lot of time alone and generally avoid the news and the media, I sometimes forget that I am not neurotypical! It can be a bit of a shock when I do go out into the real world. It did not occur to me that eating a tin of custard for breakfast, day in day out, was a bit strange, until someone found out and said it was unusual. And when people read my work, or watch one of my films, they tell me that they can definitely 'tell' *the girl with the curly hair* is not neurotypical!

ASD is difficult to explain and can be hard to understand. One problem is that it takes a lot of courage to be open and tell someone of my difficulties. The other problem is that, when I do, people do not think I "seem" autistic, or they say I do not act differently to others. I often tell people that I feel really, really anxious (and it is such a brave thing to be able to do that, it takes me a lot of courage), yet they do not seem to believe me or take my anxiety seriously. I think it is because I 'look normal' and because a lot of people are not very empathetic, not very understanding and probably do not have a sufficiently developed theory of mind.

I think a lot of people could become more empathetic and considerate of other people, whether they are autistic, neurotypical (or anything else!), just because we are all human beings.

Many humans tend to assume that fellow humans think the same way as they do, and have the same aptitudes that they have. Sometimes everyone assumes that, if you find something difficult or do something a bit differently, it must be because you lack character or are just not making the effort.

Life can be experienced very differently if a person has challenges that most other people do not face, or strengths most other people do not have.

Finally, I would like to say that, although autism is a diagnosis, it is a human condition, so a person without autism should - with an open mind and with some education - be able to relate to every aspect of the condition in a person with autism. There is no single trait that differentiates someone who is autistic and someone who is not. It is a complex disorder that has to be considered *alongside* aspects of an individual's entire life. Autism is not one single trait, thought or feeling.

I feel that one of the unique parts of the CHP work is to make people become more *aware* of some of these 'human' traits and it is this awareness that can lead to more consideration, understanding and empathy for other human beings. For example, I read a lot about other people's experiences of life. A lot of the time I do not feel or think that way, *but* it opens my mind and educates me as to how someone *else* might be feeling. This makes me a more understanding and considerate person next time I go out into the world.

I hope this book supports everyone.

the girl with the curly hair

xxx

Space for your notes

How do YOU see the world?